The Forests Of Mount Rainier National Park: A Natural History

by

William H. Moir

Printed in the United States of America by the Pacific Northwest National Parks and Forests Association, a non-profit corporation managed by a Board of Directors. Its purpose is to provide for the enhanced enjoyment and understanding of visitors to its areas of operation in the States of Washington, Oregon, Idaho, Montana, and northern California.

Published by
  The Pacific Northwest National Parks and Forests Association
  83 South King Street, Suite 212, Seattle, Washington 98104
  (206) 442-7958

Design
  Diane Lynn Converse

Photography by
  the author or Dr. Jerry F. Franklin unless noted otherwise.

Dedication

All along the road to publication, this book carries the stamp of Daniel J. "Jim" Tobin. Jim was Superintendent of Mount Rainier National Park during the research that went into the writing of the original draft. He lent his considerable support as Pacific Northwest Regional Director later, when the U.S. Forest Service first considered publication of the manuscript. It is with warm satisfaction that I realize Jim knew, before his untimely death on September 7, 1985, that the book he had pushed so hard for was finally going to be realized in print.

Jim loved the forests of Mount Rainier—the real forests about which this book supplies the "moving picture." He wanted others, and especially the park visitors, to understand and love them, too. It is therefore with affection and appreciation for his part in backing the research, the writing, and the publication, that I dedicate this book to Jim Tobin. He loved the park; he lived the park. This book helps explain why.

Preface

Sometimes we think we've heard it all. The story was explained to us years ago. Remember the first time you visited a national park and took the family to one of those campfire talks given by park rangers? All of you marveled at how the lichens grew on the rock and made an ounce of soil, which was enough for the moss to grow on. Then the moss made some more soil, and so on until finally the trees came.

By the time you hit the fifth park you knew the story by heart. We still keep hearing it. Acadia, Big Bend, the Grand Tetons, Mount Rainier. I call this level of natural history interpretation the "lichen on the rock" syndrome...the uniqueness of our most wonderful natural landscapes, described at the second grade level.

And besides, this interpretation is not true! Here at Mount Rainier, the soils drop out of the sky. What could be more fantastic than that? So let's make the story of the particular uniqueness of this park factual and up-to-date. Let's flavor it with the history of the Northwest and convey some of the excitement experienced by scientists when they acquire new insights into forest ecology. The "lichen on the rock" syndrome is dead; that story, like the Model T Ford, belongs in the museum.

This is not a tree identification book. If you don't know what a Douglas-fir tree looks like, get a field guide. Lots of good ones are available. This book is about forests: an interpretive analysis of the forest landscape. For a deeper background, I have listed in the selected bibliography some field guides and several books on the plant communities, geology, and botany of the Pacific Northwest region.

This natural history is written at an advanced level, but should present little difficulty for 80 percent of the park visitors and those who generally enjoy scientific nonfiction. To assist readers, the use of technical terms was kept to a minimum except where absolutely necessary. Most words are defined in general dictionaries; also, I have supplied a glossary. Plants have been given common names when available. These names, unfortunately, are dead ends in the botanical literature, so for anyone interested in further knowledge, their botanical names are listed in the traditional location — at the back of the book.

The chapters are presented in a logical sequence. Chapters 1 through 3 describe the forest composition and structure, Chapters 4 through 8 deal mostly with forest functions and responses. But function and structure cannot readily be separated; so a mixture of both appears in each chapter. Also, there are always a few people who do things differently, even when it comes to reading a book. The chapters can be read independently or in any order; each is, in effect, a self-contained essay.

My interpretations are based on scientific inquiry. Some of the most relevant literature for each chapter is given in the suggested further reading. But science is also imagination and educated guesswork; forest ecology is no exception. Mystery, ignorance, and speculation are the frontiers of science. Readers can expect to be left dangling by unanswered questions from time to time. Certain insights and explanations based upon limited factual data can change when more information becomes available.

The rain of ash that accompanied the eruption of Mount St. Helens in May 1980 makes amply clear that this book does not tell the end of the story. What has been suggested by inference in portions of Chapters 3 and 6 is now being studied in great detail at Mount St. Helens. Elsewhere in the Pacific Northwest, scientists are also learning more and more about the functioning and management of old-growth forests. But that astonishing eruption, the new insights about the machinery of decaying logs, and all the other wonders of scientific discovery seem to lead at last to what is ultimately unknowable.

For me, the forested landscape of Mount Rainier has been the theater to discover, discriminate, and blend together the objectively knowable and the profoundly unknowable dimensions of life, existence, and perpetual change.

Fort Collins, Colorado   William H. Moir
May 1989

Acknowledgments

This book is a product of more than four years of research on the forest ecosystems at Mount Rainier National Park. The work was sponsored by the National Park Service and the U.S. Forest Service. I was fortunate enough to be involved in some of that research and the excitement that came from it. Jim Tobin, Superintendent of the park at the time and one of the patrons of our efforts, suggested that some of the results be written for a general audience. These forests are just too marvelous to be the keepsake of scientists alone.

The staff of the National Park Service has been helpful and considerate throughout all phases of this study. I am particularly indebted to Larry Henderson, Stan Schlegel, Don Field, and the many seasonal employees. There was even a road patrol officer who, in courteous performance of his duty, issued me only a warning when I was driving too slowly, studying the trees. Those summers at Mount Rainier were delightful in large measure because of our Park Service hosts.

I was involved in the forest studies for two summers and a winter, and sundry times since. My co-workers included Mary Ayers, Don Hobson, Sarah Greene, and Miles Hemstrom; to them my thanks for their companionship and insights gained mutually about forest ecology. I am particularly grateful to Dr. Miles Hemstrom for his ideas and research results on fire and fire ecology, which I borrowed for Chapters 4 and 5.

Dr. Richard Waring introduced me to some of his ideas (since published) on the water dynamics of big trees, used in Chapter 3. Others generously contributing time and effort to portions of this project and book are Dr. Henry W. Smith, Dr. Jan Henderson, Dr. Don Mullineaux (can I ever forget that wonderful trip to your Williwaukas site?), Dr. Joe Means, Dr. Ted Thomas, and Mr. Bill Bradley.

This book did not jell easily. I am grateful for technical reviews of various parts by Mr. Chris Maser, Dr. Fred Swanson, Dr. Dwight R. Crandell, Dr. Miles Hemstrom, and Dr. Jerry F. Franklin. One of the greatest hurdles concerned how to render complex scientific subjects to a lay audience. But many difficulties seemed to vaporize when Harvey Manning read and criticized the manuscript. He encouraged me when my energy flagged. If parts of this book glitter, it's because Mr. Manning helped me. I even borrowed an episode (in Chapter 7) from one of his experiences at Mount Rainier.

Dr. Jerry F. Franklin gave unflagging encouragement and support throughout the entire project. Dr. Franklin has been the director of the forest ecosystem studies at Mount Rainier National Park. He not only made this whole thing possible, but he conveyed to all of us who worked with him the sense of excitement coming from such forest studies as described in this book.

The quotation prefacing Chapter 1 is from E. Lucy Braun, *Deciduous Forests of Eastern North America*, published by Hafner Publishing Company, 1950. The quoted excerpt prefacing Chapter 6 is from a Puyallup Indian legend retold by Ella E. Clark in *Indian Legends of the Pacific Northwest*, published by the University of California Press, Berkeley.

Valuable editorial assistance from Shirley Moore, Mr. Jim Wood and Ms. Jean Matthews is also appreciated. Jean's persistence and hard work on the word processor was the catalyzing force that transformed the manuscript into this book.

Contents

Let us envision the forest as an aggregate of plant and
animal life: an aggregate of trees of the canopy and
lower layers, shrubs and vines, both large and small,
herbaceous plants of the forest floor; mosses and
lichens on the ground, on rocks, and on tree trunks,
fungi, both parasitic and saprophytic, and also of the
animals—grazing, burrowing, leaf-eating, seed-eating
—the mammals, the birds, the insects, and the microorganisms (plant and animal) above and below ground; an
aggregate of interdependent and interacting organisms.
From among this aggregate of multitudinous forms, the
trees stand out pre-eminent, because of their superior
size and because of their pronounced influence upon all
the forest inhabitants. Yet each member of the forest
community plays its part, in competition, in contributing
to organic detritus, in giving to the forest its many
aspects, both local and seasonal.

E. Lucy Braun
1950

Figure 1. Forests frame the Mount Rainier landscape.

Chapter 1
Introduction to the Forests

As soon as we enter Mount Rainier National Park along the Nisqually River, we come to a different world. The commercial and second-growth forests are suddenly left behind. The drive to Longmire takes us through a canopied landscape of giant trees, lush vegetative understories, shade and filtered light, mossy logs, and swamps of skunk cabbage and vine maple. From afar we saw the giant, ice-laden volcano, but that's hidden now. Many visitors come to see "The Mountain," but they actually spend most of their time travelling through and viewing forests, since about 57 percent of the park is forested. Everyone speaks about the fantastic flowering meadows at Paradise, seen against the backdrop of plunging glaciers. But the forests provide a fitting prelude to this alpine experience and are also a subject of study in their own right. They are equal to the challenge of glaciers and meadows. These big trees can occupy our time in the park in many rewarding ways. It is a different world.

We proceed toward Longmire in forest scenery that is always changing. Here giant ferns appear, there an astonishing array of lush herbs (vanilla leaf, bunchberry, foamflower), now a steamy pool of vine maple and devil's club. The massive trunk of a 700-year-old Douglas-fir thrusts into a canopy that exceeds the height of a 20-story building. A shaft of sunlight catches a spray of foliage in vivid chromatic glow.

Many different kinds of forests exist in the park. The more we perceive and understand the differences, the greater is our enjoyment and sense of belonging. Generally, the forests fall into three categories—those at low elevation along the major rivers, those along the slopes and valleys at intermediate elevations, and those at the uppermost drainages and uplands of high elevations. In the next chapter we will study forest zonation more carefully. For an introduction, however, let us begin with some of the common forests in each of the three elevational zones.

Low Elevation Forests Along the Major Rivers

Our approach to Longmire was through forest mostly of the WESTERN HEMLOCK/DEVIL'S CLUB type, so named for a conspicuous tree and understory plant in the vegetation assemblage of mature or old forest stands. Some common trees of this forest type are Douglas-fir, western hemlock, western redcedar, red alder, and black cottonwood. Along this Nisqually River roadside we might catch sight, as well, of occasional crooked, mossy-stemmed trunks of bigleaf maple.

The WESTERN HEMLOCK/DEVIL'S CLUB forest is also found along the lower stretches of the Ohanapecosh River. This is an important wintering area for elk, which have consumed much of the devil's club, a preferred browse species. Here too is the famous Grove of the Patriarchs, one of the marvelous stands of this forest type. The lay visitor sees the immense western redcedars as wonders of antiquity, but ecologists ask why the huge, old specimens are not being replaced by western hemlock as normally expected in forests of this type. The grove is situated on very recent river bar soil. Nearby are pure stands of red alder. As they fringe the clear, emerald water of the Ohanapecosh, the alders provide a scenic contrast to the taller canopies of the conifers beyond. What we cannot see is the vital role these alders play in the forest ecosystem. They are converting atmospheric nitrogen, an inert gas, into ammonia and nitrate-nitrogen, essential for the ecosystem's plant growth and nutrient cycling. We'll return to this important subject in later chapters.

The Grove of the Patriarchs also is noted for the profusion and richness of understory vegetation. Among the many flowering plants and ferns growing on these moist soils are enchanter's nightshade, oak fern, lady fern, mitrewort, broadleafed montia, sweet cicely, foamflower, several kinds of violets, sword fern, betony, nodding fescue, and salmonberry. The knowledgeable botanist could tally about 70 or 80 species amidst this luxuriance, and getting down on hands and knees underneath the displays of massed leaves could discover as many species again of mosses and liverworts along the seeps and rivulets.

Some of the best stands of the WESTERN HEMLOCK/DEVIL'S CLUB forest can be seen in the Carbon River valley. The scenic impression is quite different from either the Ohanapecosh or Nisqually valleys. Old Sitka spruce join the parade of giants near the entrance station, but not for long. Douglas-fir and western redcedar have impressive girth (one Douglas-

2

Figure 2. Understory luxuriance: a thousand photosynthetic surfaces beg for sunlight near Narada Falls.

fir measures 109 inches in diameter at breast height, but is inconspicuous among its peers). Many of these trees are about 550 years old. Some are so large that roots branching from the trunk base create huge mounds that a person can climb only with great difficulty.

The forest floor is ridden with decomposing trunks of fallen giants, crisscrossed into networks of superhighways and interchanges. This down timber may represent as much biomass as 150 tons per acre—even more where tree mortality is particularly heavy (see Chapter 8). A fallen monarch conducts the eye along a mossy, elevated tramway over rooftops of devil's club and salmonberry, past highrise towers of western redcedar, to the tumbling ribbon of milky water where ominous clunking sounds come from ice-polished boulders rumbling their way to the sea. The river froths and seethes, but the vegetation of its banks

bears a timeless witness to the perseverance of life, the self-maintaining ability of complex forest ecosystems that have colonized the riverbeds and mudflows of the past and healed those once raw wounds.

In the Carbon River valley, even the devil's club is tall. Crooked stems, like immobilized troupes of belly dancers, wriggle and twist to 8 or 10 feet above their watery floors. This frenzy to reach upward is perhaps best explained by the dim illumination at the forest floor. But the rootholds too are engaged in a competitive struggle. The search for essential nutrients, such as nitrogen, or for soil oxygen is intense. Salal, so common in certain other forest types, is crowded onto the upper surfaces of fallen logs or the higher, drier summits of root mounds. On such microhabitats salal can compete better for its required light and nourishment than in the wetter sites, where devil's club, skunk cabbage and ferns hold the competitive edge.

*Figure 3. Along the canopied lushness near Tahoma Creek, the park visitor is embraced
by old-growth stands of Douglas-fir, western redcedar, and western hemlock.
(Photo courtesy National Park Service)*

So numerous are the subtle variations in the WESTERN HEMLOCK/ DEVIL'S CLUB forest that they almost defy a precise definition of the forest's vegetation composition. Each of the major valleys around Mount Rainier has its own variations. Along the Mowich and Carbon rivers, the foamflower is mostly the three-leaflet type (*Tiarella trifoliata*), rather than the one-leaflet form (*T. unifoliata*) found so luxuriant in the understory along the Nisqually or Tahoma Creek. Gentle streamlets carrying snow meltwaters from adjoining slopes across cobbly terraces of the Carbon or Puyallup rivers are almost succulent with the verdure of twisted stalk or Scouler's corydalis. Lovely groves of grand fir stand near the White River. Profusions of mixed fern populations (oak fern, sword fern, deer fern, lady fern) are seen in unrivaled display along lower Tahoma Creek. With such compositional variations, the best generalizing features of the WESTERN HEMLOCK/DEVIL'S CLUB forest type are (1) the valley bottom location, (2) the luxuriance in understory vegetation of both shrubs and herbs, (3) the presence, usually conspicuous, of devil's club, and (4) the absence or rarity of silver fir in tree populations.

Forests of Slopes and Valleys at Intermediate Elevations

In forests higher on the slopes of Rainier and adjoining ridges, other trees become increasingly common. To be sure, Douglas-fir, western hemlock, and western redcedar still abound, but now we see increasing numbers of silver and noble firs and Alaska yellow-cedar. Along principal valley bottoms, but also on seepy or soggy slopes, the WESTERN HEMLOCK/ DEVIL'S CLUB forests gradually blend to a SILVER FIR/DEVIL'S CLUB forest that differs mainly in the greater abundance of silver fir. To identify it, hikers needn't muddy their boots lunging into this forest— the profuse growth of devil's club, ferns, and flowering plants can be recognized from a distance.

The most common forest at elevations generally between 2500 and 4000 feet is the SILVER FIR/ALASKA HUCKLEBERRY type. We see it along the East Side Trail, Owyhigh Lakes Trail, Ipsut Creek Trail, along Olallie Creek, and along many segments of the Wonderland Trail. As with forests of the low valleys, there is much variation in the plant composition. The trail hiker, however, is soon aware of the most definitive attribute: the omnipresence of huckleberry shrubs, sometimes in conjunction with vine maple, sometimes not. Often there are four

different huckleberries: the black (big leaf), oval-leaf, red, and Alaska. The Alaska huckleberry is usually most abundant. Under the sometimes continuous layer of huckleberry canopy is a moss-covered floor studded with low, evergreen, shiny-leaved herbs: twinflower, several species of wintergreen, bunchberry, pipsissewa, Oregon grape. From the perspective of this carpet of greenery, the hiker sees, far above, the lichen-coated branches and green canopy...two green tiers, fastened together with straight, giant bolts—the stems of silver fir, western hemlock, and here and there a superbolt of Douglas-fir or western redcedar. Occasionally, the trail crew must cut away a section of some immense trunk fallen across the path; the curious visitor can then do some tree ring counting. In places, 700 or more annular rings can be discerned, particularly if the tree happens to be Douglas-fir.

The SILVER FIR/ALASKA HUCKLEBERRY forest is never uniform. Talus slides or snow avalanche tracks interrupt it. Or perhaps the more open-canopied old stands are broken by fires which give rise to denser, closer canopied second-growth stands, described in more detail in Chapter 5. Where soils are poorly drained, we can find an increased abundance of Alaska yellow-cedar; but on still wetter soils, such as those on wet, seepy slopes, benches, or drainages, forests of the SILVER FIR/DEVIL'S CLUB type interrupt. At higher elevations, when cooler temperatures cause snow to linger longer, the SILVER FIR/ALASKA HUCKLEBERRY forest may feature abundant low plants at the moss level, particularly strawberry-leaf blackberry and twisted stalk that are not common in more typical stands. At the opposite environmental extreme—the drier, more sunny exposures at low elevations—we find less huckleberry and much more Oregon grape.

A thousand images, sounds, moods, and impressions come with the trails through SILVER FIR/ ALASKA HUCKLEBERRY forest. There are sudden surprises: a spotted owl flushed from a low branch, some elk startled during their feast on huckleberry browse, the turbulent plume of mist from a plunge pool, the twittery, inquisitive visit from a family of boreal chickadees as we take lunch break near a soft, mossy log. Most of these images, wildlife encounters, and other experiences of the forest environment are typically Cascadian because the SILVER FIR/ ALASKA HUCKLEBERRY forest type is widespread in the mountains of western Washington and Oregon.

A sharply contrasting forest of intermediate elevation is the SILVER FIR/FOAMFLOWER type. One of its most conspicuous trees is noble fir; its platy, purple bark stands out among the silvery, lichen-draped stems of silver fir. Seen from afar, the bluish canopy of noble fir crowns is easily distinguishable from the green or yellow-green crowns of other conifers. Since it is a relatively intolerant tree (that is, it requires high light intensity on the forest floor for effective germination and seedling survival and growth), noble fir often attests to past fires (Chapter 4) which created openings where even-aged stands became established. We can see a rectangular patch of even-aged noble fir on the southeast-facing slopes of the White River drainage below Sunrise Ridge. After about 350 years, however, the noble fir has mostly died out, so that stands of SILVER FIR/FOAM-FLOWER type consist mostly of silver fir and a few large Douglas-fir or western hemlock.

The SILVER FIR/FOAMFLOWER forest prefers warm, sunny sites with deep, well-drained soils. Most park visitors harbor notions about the process of soil formation as a long, slow process of weathering and organic buildup from residual rocks. But many of the soils in the Cascades are formed of materials that dropped out of the sky when volcanoes coughed and gasped in numerous convulsive episodes. The whitish or yellowish sands blown in from Mount St. Helens are seen in trail cuts, and layer upon layer of ash from several eruptive sources usually make up the deep soils of the SILVER FIR/FOAMFLOWER forest. Sometimes the ash layers are thinner or washed downslope, leaving a cobbly residue that is often indicated by thickets of vine maple.

Another of the distinctive features of SILVER FIR/FOAMFLOWER forest is the wealth of herbaceous plants of the forest floor. The shrubs we encounter in the SILVER FIR/ALASKA HUCKLE-BERRY type abruptly give way to an extravagance of herbs. Foamflower, vanilla leaf, twisted stalk, false solomon's seal, arnica, beadlily, and oak fern, alone or in combination, mask the forest floor under dense sheets of foliage. Patches of herbs composed of different combinations of plants occur in kaleidoscopic variation. Everywhere the geometry of leaf display is amazingly precise and well structured. Each leaf and leaflet has its own space; unused space doesn't exist. Every beam of light penetrating the tree canopy finds a billion outstretched, begging surfaces eager to prevent its falling wasted on some detrital area. Our footsteps temporarily disorder this leafy array; a wake of bent or crushed herbage is the price of serendipitous wandering. But our steps miss more stems than not, and the momentary disturbance of our passage is readily readjusted. After tremulous reproach our path refills with geometric green.

Forests at High Elevations

As we drive higher onto the flanks of the great volcano the forest mood changes. Up here, forests are very different. Trees of impressive stature at lower elevations are now considerably reduced in height. Forest closure seems almost everywhere broken by snow avalanche tracks, subalpine meadows, cascades, and glacial lakes. Lobes of massive glaciers intrude ponderous, boulder-laden masses in radial, spider-like geometry down the volcano cone. Alternating with the glaciers are rolling uplands formed of ancient Rainier lavas where trees are thinly scattered or precariously confined to rocky perches of lesser snow burden. This is the backcountry, the subalpine, the place of awesome mountain scenery, of clouds and fogs and unpredictable snowstorms, where snow can persist through August, where the soils are almost always saturated, and where the trees are distorted and hardened by the hostile high elevation climate.

Principal trees at elevations generally above 4000 feet are silver fir, subalpine fir, Alaska yellow-cedar, and mountain hemlock. At about 5500 feet, the closed forest breaks up into mosaics of meadows and forest islands known to ecologists as the forest-tundra ecotone and to most visitors as subalpine parkland. We'll see in Chapter 7 how the subalpine parkland is an arena where forest advance or dieback is sensitive to changes of climate. Some trees rather special to the upper edge of closed forest and subalpine parkland are whitebark pine and, at a few locations, lodgepole pine.

Some of the commonly encountered forests include the SILVER FIR/RUSTY LEAF and the SILVER FIR/RHODODENDRON types, again named for a leading tree and understory plant of mature or old forests. Important shrubs of these communities include the Alaska and oval-leaf huckleberries, black huckleberry, white-flowered rhododendron, and rusty leaf (sometimes known as fool's huckleberry). In the Golden Lakes region where fires have swept across the uplands, these shrubs comprise impenetrable tangles between snags of the former forest. Old-growth forests of shrub-dominated understories can be found at Mowich Lake, upper Huckleberry Creek, Cayuse Pass, and Narada Falls.

Spring arrives late. As winter snow melts, the fawnlilies follow with their new spring "snow," those carpets of nodding white beneath the shrubs not yet fully leafed out. Other herbs of the forest floor are also soon in flower: twisted stalk, trailing raspberries (*Rubus pedatus* and *R. lasiococcus*), and yellow violet (*Viola sempervirens*). But these herbs are usually few in number of species, for not many endure so long under the snowpack. In some areas, indeed, where several years of snowpack might persist, the herb and shrub populations might be wiped out. Ecologists have not yet worked out just how long the various plants can remain buried under snow. But as we hike through these high elevation forests we observe here a patch where fawnlilies and other herbs are plentiful and there a thicket of shrubs without many herbs, and at still another location both shrubs and herbs in profusion. Could this patchiness reveal the varying depths of snowpack in these forests?

Vertical drainage in soils of both SILVER FIR/RUSTY LEAF and SILVER FIR/RHODODEN-DRON forests is restricted by an iron pan horizon. This is a soil layer cemented by iron oxides. We're not sure how it develops, but the lateral movement of soil water between volcanic ash layers of different textures may be responsible. Dissolved iron minerals in this water gradually build up and clog the pores of the soil space. Vertical drainage is then further restricted and the lateral water movement brought closer to the surface. Iron pan horizons can vary from extremely hard and thick to rather interrupted, thinner, or only moderately hard. Roots cannot penetrate the thicker, more cemented pans. Thus, meltwater or rainfall percolation and runoff—and roots—are restricted to the uppermost mineral soil and organic layers. The decomposition of humus is slower on saturated, poorly aerated, and cold soils and the accumulation of black humus may exceed four or five inches at some iron pan sites. The trails along these pan soils are commonly mucky. Campsites are difficult for rangers and hikers to locate because of soil saturation; close attention to drainage patterns is needed. It's one thing to slog over the pan soils and quite another to sleep on them.

The picturesque character of high elevation forests makes our visit worthwhile, despite bad weather. How many photos of the icefields are framed by gnarled, fuzzy branches of mountain hemlock? The droopy, forlorn appearance of Alaska yellow-cedars reflect our shivering misery and disappointment when the summit is shrouded in bleak gray. Suppose the subalpine lakes were not rimmed and framed by graceful spires of subalpine fir. Would Yakima Park be less than perfect without the copses of subalpine fir and whitebark pine?

The wet, dripping foliage of the shrubs and tree canopies has soaked many pairs of hiking socks, caused many a blister, and bounced rain in drumming rhythms on the nylon or canvas shelters of high country campers. In a kind of perverse mockery, the forests and saturated soils of these high elevations extend cool and limited hospitality to those seeking refuge from the austere climates of the meadows and icelands of higher slopes. But even as we retreat to lower elevations and more amenable climates, we carry with us the sense of these trees and forest communities—continuing their stands day after day, year after year, storm after storm. Defiant, hardy, unyielding. The images of those drippy or snow-laden canopies, now fading into the mist as we descend, will remain with us forever. Forest life is incredibly tenacious.

Chapter 2
Forest Landscapes

I was in one of the plush, carpeted offices of the National Science Foundation in Washington, D. C. —and totally out of my element. Jerry Franklin had just thrown me a bombshell. The National Park Service wanted him to conduct a forest study of Mount Rainier National Park, and he was asking if I would head the field aspects of this study during the first summer.

All I knew about the park was that it contained a huge volcano on whose icy slopes it rained or snowed all the time.

About 200 square miles of forest cloak the lower slopes of that volcano. As Jerry was explaining, the project mission was to describe those forests and characterize their habitats, their distribution within the park, their disturbance histories, and the patterns of forest succession that followed these disturbances. That's all!

I was thinking about rain and more rain. And dark, gloomy forests unvisited and undescribed, thriving in some of the most inaccessible and rugged backcountry of the Cascade Range. I was skeptical that these forests could be differentiated and classified. This was taking a cold, dark bull by the horns—hardly alluring to a guy living in sunny, southern New Mexico. I accepted.

Readers, beware. In this chapter I will toss you the full spectrum of forest patterns at Mount Rainier National Park, as perceived not just by myself but by numerous co-workers on this project. It took us more than three years and a lot of computer analysis, several dissertations and theses, and various revisions and refinements of our forest concepts to become satisfied that the forest patterns and habitat relationships make much sense. How can I cover 200 square miles of forest complexity in about 30 minutes or less of reading time? To make the subject more palatable, I have divided this chapter into two parts. The first will give you, I hope, some insights as to how we went about studying the forests; the second part summarizes forest zones and patterns in various sectors of the park. Later chapters will deal with the disturbance histories and how the forests respond to those disturbances.

Part 1. The Traverse

Sarah was oiling her boots in the luxury of our apartment at Ohanapecosh Ranger Station in the southeast sector of the park while I pored over dozens of air photos of the park. Tomorrow was July fourth; the park would be full of tourists, and we wanted to escape the hassle. Heading into the backcountry and leaving the crowded roads and trails behind was an ideal way to warm up to the summer's work. As I studied the canopied expanses on sheet after sheet of photos, a giddy sensation came over me. The enormity of the job, spread before me as mile after mile of both closed and open canopies, taunted me with mystery. Since much of the forested landscape was both rugged and remote, the first problem would be just getting there. I was looking at whole valleys and major drainage systems where no man-made path existed. One major tool for the summer would be the boots that Sarah was working on.

I settled for an air photo sheet that revealed striking forest mosaics along lower Panther Creek and along slopes just south of the creek. The photo showed mature or old-growth forest as pebbly, coarse-grained canopy, and irregular boundaries to young forests as smooth, fine-grained canopies. Was this boundary a fire line, and if so, when did the fire occur? A heart-shaped meadow in the middle of the fine-grained canopy was apparently being invaded by trees. What kind of trees, and why were they invading? What was the ground cover in the meadow? Would this cover be the same beneath the adjoining closed forest? Another abrupt boundary in canopy graininess separated the closed forests on west-facing slopes, and what appeared to be old-growth stands descended from about midslope all the way to the highway. I had no idea what kind of forests these were.

We spent the evening assembling gear. Topo maps, compass, increment borer, waterproof notebook, diameter tape, hand lens, binoculars, shovel, pencils, knife, tape measure, meter stick, data sheets, and— "Hey, Sarah, what have we forgotten?" Toilet paper, insect dope, extra socks, sweater, rain coat, candy bars, first aid kit (check to see if any bandages are left), altimeter. Where's my cap? Thank goodness it's only a one-day trip; this early in the season it was still hard to get our act together. If anything's forgotten, we'll know tomorrow. Hell with it, I'm going to bed...I wonder if I remembered the matches?

The best way to inventory forests is to get into them on foot. Our procedure was to travel a slope, trail, road segment, or whatever path through a forested landscape and establish a string of vegetation plots that reflect both typical and changing forest patterns along that path. The traversed path would span the important discontinuities of the landscape, especially the variations in soils, positions in the landscape (e.g. valley bottoms, lower and upper slopes, ridgetops), exposures (elevation, steepness and direction of slope), and landforms (terrain of distinct geological origin such as river terraces, mudflows, glacial moraine, or water-carved sideslopes). We believed these to be some of the principal environmental features that could relate in some way to observed shifts in the composition of forest vegetation. Concerning the vegetation, we knew that we could not keep track of all the plant species simultaneously; there were simply too many. It is more practical, as well as ecologically meaningful, to pay attention just to the dominant species (that is, the most important plants in each of the tree, shrub, and herb layers as determined by their cover or density). Whenever we detected some kind of shift in the cover or density in any of the dominant plants, we would then measure the cover or density of all the trees, shrubs, and herbs in some plot within the new forest vegetation. Our plots were mostly circular in shape and 500 square meters in size (or .12 acre). The reader need not be bothered with technical details of plot location or measurements. It is sufficient to regard the plot as a sample of the forest stand which reflects the essential dominance relationships of the plants in the stand as well as the characteristic environmental features. We also recorded anything special about the stand, such as wildlife use of browse plants, evidence of fire, unusual tree mortality from insects, or whatever.

The Fourth of July begins in solemn overcast and total humidity, but at least it isn't raining. We start our traverse at the switchback at about 3800 feet in elevation, along the Shriner Peak Trail. We then leave the trail and descend into the valley. Our first objective is a patch of old growth north of the creek, about 700 feet below us. Great gullies descend the burned slopes of Shriner Peak, and it is easy enough for us to lose elevation. All we have to do is avoid confrontation with vine maple, sticky laurel, and alder thickets, but there are plenty of openings where bracken fern leads the way. A whiff of elk or deer musk catches us, but the animals remain hidden. I see a pair of western bluebirds flying off a dead tree, and

several hawks eyeballing these burned-over slopes. We work our way across a few more gullies and soon enter thickets of sapling western hemlocks. Just beyond looms a wall of old-growth forest, which we enter after being slapped in the face by whips of impudent hemlock.

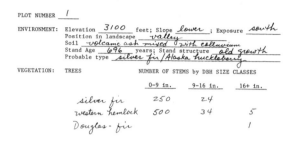

FIELD DATA

PLOT NUMBER _1_

ENVIRONMENT: Elevation _3100_ feet; Slope _lower_ ; Exposure _south_
Position in landscape _valley_
Soil _volcanic ash mixed with colluvium_
Stand Age _696_ years; Stand structure _old growth_
Probable type _silver fir/Alaska huckleberry_

VEGETATION: TREES   NUMBER OF STEMS by DBH SIZE CLASSES

	0-9 in.	9-16 in.	16+ in.
silver fir	250	24	
western hemlock	500	34	5
Douglas-fir			1

UNDERSTORY SHRUBS AND HERBS (Canopy coverage as %)

Vine maple (8)   false solomon seal (1)
bunchberry (4)   trailing raspberry (1)
Alaska huckleberry (3) pipsissewa (1)
black huckleberry (1)   Oregon grape (trace)
                        dewberry (trace)

OTHER FEATURES:
Originated by fire

INTERPRETATION: dry variation of the _silver fir/Alaska huckleberry_ forest type because of low elevation and south-facing slope. Absence of salal and only trace cover of Oregon grape preclude assignment to _silver fir/Oregon grape_ type.

Finished with data collection at last, Sarah and I are getting impatient to move on. The morning is getting old and we have scarcely begun our traverse. Further slopes promise plenty of forest excitement, but first there is the river to negotiate.

We approach the cliffs about 40 feet above Panther Creek and look down. The noise is thunderous, and I have to shout to her at my side. "What do we do now?" We gaze down on the frothing whitewater. I think about the subtle difference between challenge and threat. Confined to a deep, narrow gorge, the waters vented their fury in a turbulence that would have been merely awesome if we did not have to cross it; but it was terrifying because we did. "Let's look for a log," Sarah replies. She starts upstream, above the cliffs, while I search the other way. We rejoin about a half hour later. "Any luck?" we ask each other. No log bridges in Sarah's direction; I'd found only a narrow pole spanning the chasm about 15 feet above the water. We don't have a rope, and I don't relish the thought of so precarious a tightrope dance with the furies. When Sarah sees the log she echoes my sentiments: "Let's look some more." But further search proves futile; either we cross on that pole, or the whole traverse is over, here and now.

I look at the old growth above the cliffs on the other side—so mysterious, so beckoning, so very near. I look at the roaring river below the log, and then again at the forest beyond. I swallow my fear. Long pause. More fear to swallow. "Let's go!"

There are three rules to think about in river crossing when the element of danger is high. First, don't do it. Second, if you have to do it, be absolutely convinced there's no other safer, better alternative whatsoever. Third, when your mind is steeled to the absolute necessity, then go ahead, but GO, no matter how—by straddling, crawling, balancing on foot, however. Above all, don't hesitate, pause, look down, or think about anything except getting to the other side as soon as possible.

We make it. Scrambling up cliffs and very steep slopes, we are soon within the forest that had caught my imagination on the air photo sheet and had lured us across the river. Its mystery surrounds us. To Sarah's astonishment, I am reveling in the wet, slippery slopes and thickets of devil's club. We have gained 400 feet in elevation from our river crossing, and I can stand it no longer. "Let's take a plot."

FIELD DATA

PLOT NUMBER __2__

ENVIRONMENT: Elevation __3200__ feet; Slope __lower__ ; Exposure __north__
Position in landscape __lower valley slope__
Soil __wet, extremely cobbly skeletal colluvium__
Stand Age __700__ years; Stand structure __old growth__
Probable type __silver fir / devil's club__

VEGETATION: TREES

	NUMBER OF STEMS by DBH SIZE CLASSES		
	0-9 in.	9-16 in.	16+ in.
western redcedar			1
western hemlock	34	1	1
silver fir	4	1	1

UNDERSTORY SHRUBS AND HERBS (Canopy coverage as %)

Devil's club (40)	oak fern (90)
salmonberry (4)	foamflower (16)
vine maple (3)	stream violet (8)
yew (5)	lady fern (7)

OTHER FEATURES: Well-trodden elk paths here. Important food, judging from clipped plants, include salmonberry, vine maple, devil's club.

INTERPRETATION: This is a typical silver fir / devil's club forest of cool, wet slopes.

Lunch time, but choosing a comfortable site on these steep slopes is difficult. The bristling, prickly devil's club doesn't invite our intimate proximity, while unarmed plants are in mucky places. But near the base of a large western redcedar we find a dry site with a needle-mat carpet, which is cozy enough if we sweep away some of the elk pellets. I like lunch break. It's time to enjoy the forest scene in its entirety—the sounds, the aromas, the impressions of form and structure, the tiny moss nearby with delicate, transparent leaflike appendages, the many manifestations of hidden forest life (I wonder where that big black ant came from—how quickly she found my cracker crumb). Few of these realities of the forest show up in the numbers on the data sheets. Lunch is time to expand our minds as well as stomachs.

Too soon it's time to continue. Packs are readjusted, and our bodies begrudgingly transpose from the soporific pleasantries of lunch back to chugging exertions on steep slopes. And steep they are—about 70 percent slope (for every 100 feet of horizontal distance we gain 70 feet of elevation). To keep from slipping, our progress is aided by welcomed handholds of firmly rooted vine maple and yew. We cannot ascend more easily by switchback, since thickets of devil's club and dense maple bar the way.

Above is a series of rock ledges that look treacherous; we'll have to find an elk trail that leads above. There are none. We detour along the base of the ledges seeking some feasible way up. Still no elk trails. Sarah finds a vague route that seems to go, while I, not wanting her rocks bouncing off my head, find another.

Carefully we work our way above the ledges, using woody handholds whenever possible. Those shrubs are not all that hospitable and have ways of getting back at us for seemingly trying to uproot them as we lunge upward. They attack face and shoulders or, as a last resort, hook into the pack. At that the battle is joined: forward progress meets increasing resistance of the flexed branch. Stalemate. The adversaries are locked in motionless tension. Breathing hard on this precarious slope, I reach over my head in an attempt to unhook an offending limb. My left foot slips, and the shovel held in the other hand drops as I react to gain foothold. It shoots downslope in reckless abandon. Clang! The blade rebounds off a rock and the handle careens into a sapling. The shovel disappears over the ledges. Clang! It hits somewhere on the rocky slope below. There's a sound of dislodged stones tumbling down the ledge, and finally silence.

Damnation! Now I must extricate myself and yield that hard-earned elevation in order to retrieve the shovel. Slowly I back down, and the limb eases pressure. Then both my feet slip, and I'm catapulted downslope. About 20 feet below I perceive out of the jerky, blurry images of my bumpy descent the limb of a yew just above those ledges over which the shovel disappeared. With the timing of a trapeze artist I grab that limb as I pass beneath. The limb bows madly— will it break? It holds; my momentum is arrested. Thus suspended, I find my relief is tempered with defeat and humiliation. These valleys are vicious— how do I get out of this mess?

Elevation: 3380 ft. Position: midslope above cliffs and ledges. Slope: 55%. Exposure: north

Old-growth forest here is drier, the understory vegetation more sparse. The combined cover of shrub dominants (Alaska, oval-leaf, and red huckleberries) is only 4%. Oregon grape is infrequent. No sign of elk.

Elevation: 3500 ft. Slope is still steep, but compass now reads 285 degrees azimuth indicating a west-facing slope. This is probably the silver fir/Oregon grape forest type. The major reproducing trees are western hemlock and (fewer) silver fir.

A fire line is here. Below it are large trees with open canopy; above are smaller trees around 15 inches diameter, almost all Douglas-fir. One specimen is measured at 15.4 inches dbh and 110 years old. The overstory canopy above the fire line is closed. The fire line is not sharp, since some older, larger trees are seen among the poles, and occasional poles (9-16 in. dbh) are fingering below the line into the older forest.

Our progress is easier, although the slope is still steep. But the rough terrain of cliffs and ledges is now behind, so we're more relaxed. Sarah and I continue upslope away from the fire line. This new forest we have entered confuses me; I cannot decide just what type it is. In certain features it resembles the SILVER FIR/ALASKA HUCKLEBERRY type with sparse understory that we passed at 3380 feet. But here the cover of black huckleberry is greater, and there's more beargrass too—some of the characteristics of the SILVER FIR/BEARGRASS type. We could be in an area of overlap between these two forest types, a transition zone, an ecotone. The change in the forest age also confuses matters, since stands on either side of the fire line are in different stages of development (see Chapter 5). The best thing would be to get away from this age-mixture of trees near the fire line and possible ecotone area and see what lies beyond. We keep going upslope, alert now for shifts in the

composition of dominant trees, shrubs, or herbs. Shortly we come to a stand where the vegetation definitely takes a new appearance. Is this the type that was first suggested near the fire line? Black huckleberry now is dominant, but why is beargrass still minor? What type is this? What's the soil like here? When the questions outweigh the answers, it's time for a plot.

Concluding our observations, the two of us head for the ridge above. After great labor and some huffing and puffing we sit down on this ridgetop, which turns out to be a broad rib descending from still higher slopes. We're now a thousand feet above the

PLOT NUMBER __3__

ENVIRONMENT: Elevation __3600__ feet; Slope __steep__; Exposure __north__
Position in landscape __upper side slope__
Soil __tephra with minimum development__
Stand Age __ca. 200__ years; Stand structure __closed poles (80% cover)__
Probable type __uncertain__

VEGETATION: TREES

	NUMBER OF STEMS by DBH SIZE CLASSES		
	0-9 in.	9-16 in.	16+ in.
western hemlock	15	8	1
Douglas-fir	2	16	1
silver fir	24	1	
western red cedar	1	+ (outside plot)	

UNDERSTORY SHRUBS AND HERBS (Canopy coverage as %)

black huckleberry (8)	bunchberry (2)
Alaska huckleberry (4)	trailing raspberry (2)
yew (4)	vanilla leaf (1)
rhododendron (2)	beargrass (1)

OTHER FEATURES:

INTERPRETATION: *This stand occurs in a concave drainage and appears to have been modified by fire about 200 years ago. Large western hemlocks (30-35 inches dbh) may have been spared, while a few pole Douglas-fir (9-16 in.) came in subsequently. Both rhododendron and trailing raspberry hint that this north-facing drainage receives more snowpack or subsurface runoff than adjoining slopes. There's too little beargrass and too much Alaska huckleberry to qualify this stand as the silver fir/beargrass type. Could this plot represent a new type?*

river crossing but can still easily hear the whitewater. The glory of the view preempts speech. We can look directly up the wild upper Ohanapecosh Valley and see the lower masses of the Whitman, Ohanapecosh, and Fryingpan glaciers disappearing into roiling clouds. The clouds obscure the volcano cone except for where, unbelievably far above, at cloud top and almost appearing as one of them, the dome of Columbia Crest seems to float. At mid-distance, the spires of the

Cowlitz Chimneys are wrapped in hovering, wispy patches of mist. To our north is Shriner Peak, well below cloud level. The deep forms of the Ohanapecosh Valley and its major tributaries—Panther, Chinook, and Olallie creeks—are easily identified. From the detached summit to the dark, forested valley bottoms, the scale and distance of the scene to our west is, quite simply, stupendous. We could stay here for hours, but there is work to do.

Immediately before us to the south is that heart-shaped meadow, no more an abstraction on an air photo, but a reality necessitating our withdrawal from that narcotic view. The meadow, we discover, is dominated by beargrass; also there is bracken fern and black huckleberry. The loose, sandy soil is much disturbed by elk and deer. One thing is certain: those animals did not get here the way we did. Isolated trees are western hemlock, Douglas-fir, a couple of western white pine, some small noble fir. Basically, however, it's a meadow; the trees are not very important. This gentle, west-facing slope so near the ridge conveys the impression of a hot, dry exposure far different from our earlier slopes. The meadow is bounded to the south by a deep ravine densely forested on the other side. We cross, and find ourselves in a dark thicket of Douglas-fir poles, all nearly identical in height and size. This is one of the stands whose canopy was fine-grained on the air photo. There is no way for Sarah and me to identify the forest type, for plant indicators are absent from the heavily shaded understory. The thicket appears gloomy and sterile, with little to be learned except its fire origin, so we hasten back to the meadow and follow it downslope, now heading west.

At the lower edge of the meadow we use the increment corer to age one of the Douglas-fir poles and find it to be about 125 years old (see Chapter 4). There is still plenty of beargrass here; we surmise that the potential forest, eventually to take over this meadow, would be the SILVER FIR/BEARGRASS type, assuming that centuries of forest development could occur without another fire.

Normally, this forest type occurs at much higher elevations on relatively dry exposures. It's possible that beargrass flourishes in the meadow here primarily because the meadow is open and sunny, and the beargrass will decline when trees control the site. Unfortunately, this meadow and the adjoining pole thickets are much too young in the sequence of forest succession (Chapter 5) for us to get an insight into the nature of whatever forest would be growing here in three or four centuries. And we are not going to wait around; it's already getting late.

We re-enter old forests on steep slopes again, having just crossed the fire line somewhat downslope from the meadow edge. I want to draw the fire line on the map and now realize that Sarah and I have not consulted the map in almost an hour. Where are we? A compass reading shows the fall line of this slope to be almost due west. We study the topo map—we must be here where the contour lines are close together, indicating steep slopes that are descending west. The map shows a major gully to our left (south) and not far. We descend that way and soon come to the gully; our location on the map is confirmed. We are here; the fire line and the meadow were there, about 3600 feet from where the slope changes from gentle to steep. Thus oriented, we feel good—this is really a great forest.

After six hundred feet of jolting motion on steep slopes, followed by log and gully hurdles on this flat bench, my knees are getting sore. Since leaving the meadow we have been in 700-year-old forest of only two types, both familiar to us, but not of sufficient novelty to justify obtaining detailed plot data. It's late afternoon now and the magnificence of these stands is competing with the weariness of body and mind. At length we come to the edge of this bench where abruptly the slope becomes steep. Consulting the map, we learn that Panther Creek is about 500 feet below and the highway a hard cross-country half mile or so to the west. About now I could enjoy a frosty glass of beer. "Hey, Will, how about a super Waldorf salad and sour cream enchilada for dinner?" Sarah asks. "Sure. How would that go with the fresh blueberry pie I was thinking about for dessert?" "A la mode, I suppose," Sarah replies as we descend into the implacable, shrubby slopes below.

In traversing such terrain as this, great penalty can attend a heedless mistake. Absorbed by epicurean pipe dreams and an eagerness to reach the highway, we have blundered. We read the map but neglected to take a compass bearing on the slope we had just entered. All too soon we are in trouble: the slope becomes steep and then extremely steep, while the menacing thickets of sapling cedar and hemlocks and shrubs of yew and maple are competing with each other and with us for footholds on precipitous ledges. By the time we realize our error, we are trapped in these thickets. Another hasty consultation with map and compass shows us perched near the edge of 300-foot cliffs that comprise the south wall of Panther Creek gorge. All too clearly now, we can hear the surging waters below us. Instead of travelling northwest as we did, we should have descended from the bench in a direction slightly south of west. Further, to correct our error by contouring this slope would

12

probably be suicidal; according to the map we have no choice but to go back up where we started, and that means regaining those 200 feet of elevation—and fighting thickets in an uphill battle. It takes almost half an hour to get back. I am nearly wiped out by fatigue and scarcely consoled that for the second time the river has failed to claim either of us. Sometimes the land can be forgiving.

A large hawk shrills at us in great agitation. "Kee-Kee-Kee ... Kee-Kee-Kee." We are heading down more gentle slopes now, and at first I can't see the hawk because the Douglas-fir and hemlocks are just too tall. "Kee-Kee-Kee," and then I spot some motion disappearing around the far side of that tall canopy over there. Soon the bird reappears—no, there are two of them—quick wingbeats alternating with short soars, and looping around us at midcanopy level about 150 feet above. The hawks disappear again through the canopy foliage; they are circling us, their high-pitched protests leaving no doubt about their displeasure. My pulse quickens as one of them glides into full view. Those wingtips are rounded, not pointed; that eliminates the falcons, such as the sharp-shinned hawk which is rather common. The bird is very big, about crow-sized, which eliminates the Cooper's hawk. "Kee-Kee-Kee-Kee ... Get-Out-Of-Here!" It could be only one bird—I am almost breathless—the goshawk, one of the rarest of accipiter hawks and to me the epitome of remote forested wilderness. Never before have I seen a goshawk. Quickly the pack comes off and my binoculars are readied. I want to study these birds and be sure of my identification. One of them alights on a tall, dead tree and I suspect its nest is not far away. I know so little about these rare hawks, but how exciting to watch them exhibit their agitation over our trespass on their nesting territory. Later I would learn more about them—that they are among the largest of the diurnal canopy and forest predators, capable, for example, of hunting squirrels or plummeting upon grouse and carrying them to the ground as their ancestors did in feudal days when the oriental art of falconry flourished. One of the birds flies out of its canopy perch to check up on us, rounded wings again displayed, and now we can see the feathers just before the tail, cottony white. Soon both birds retreat to hidden canopy places where they can watch us through the foliage without themselves being in clear view. Their shrieking ceases; they seem to know that we are but momentary intruders, that such forests as these are not places where people remain very long. Yes, my friends, I think, but are you aware that the species of man can take such forests and reduce them to

clearcuts? Where do you nest then? At least you chose well to find this forest within a national park sanctuary—there's lots of room for you. We'll leave you alone now, and not report your whereabouts. "Kee-Kee-Kee!" is all the gratitude that reaches us as we leave this wonderful place.

After a while, the slopes level off and we reach the valley. Since the bottoms of valleys receive additional moisture by way of runoff, it is not unusual for us to find numerous small creeks and seeps here. We are concluding our traverse through mosaics of SILVER FIR/DEVIL'S CLUB and ALASKA HUCKLEBERRY forest types. Verdant mixtures of devil's club and ferns grow in the lower, wetter areas of this hummocky terrain, while thickets of huckleberry and fool's huckleberry are found on rises of somewhat drier soils. Most impressive is the stature of silver fir, which we have been seeing most of the day as seedlings of understory trees. But here they are of respectable girth and reach heights in excess of 200 feet (it is hard for me to judge a tree's height more precisely when they get this tall). I check the altimeter: 2350 feet elevation. The two of us stop near a little creek to drink. The cold water makes gentle gurgling sounds where it eddies around the end of a broken log projecting into the creek. In drinking we momentarily become part of the great circulation system of this landscape we have been in all afternoon. The water is an exquisite, silvery thread, initiated on slopes at high elevations, processed through canopies, percolated around roots, ascended within stems and green leaves, condensed as dew or cloud, and again returned and filtered into the land—to emerge downslope as gentle trickles for other life-sustaining diversions or to be relinquished to the Ohanapecosh River. We are refreshed and—rather reluctantly—ready to go.

It is not long before we hear the first car speeding along the highway. As its sound grows to a crescendo, echoed and accentuated by walls of trees, and then fades into the distance, the spell of the forest is broken. Our vehicle is about two miles up the road near the Shriner Peak trailhead, but we will no longer be taking notes about the forest. The traverse is over, and we are hungry.

Part 2. Zones and Patterns

The forests at Mount Rainier National Park extend from about 1700 to 5500 feet in elevation. Over this elevational range occurs a zonation of forests controlled primarily by the changing climates. Since the massif of the Rainier volcano is approximately a geometrical cone, one might expect forests to be distributed in more or less parallel belts around the circumference of the summit cone. But Rainier, as we shall see, followed a different pattern.

Going up a mountain is like going to the North Pole. This analogy between vertical zonation of vegetation and latitudinal, climatic zones of the earth's surface attracted attention in 1889 when distributional patterns of floras and faunas were studied within the Division of Ornithology and Mammalogy of the U.S. Department of Agriculture (USDA). Dozens of treatises had appeared by then proposing divisions of North America into various biological regions. The USDA was interested in determining life zone boundaries as keys to the kinds of agricultural systems that would be feasible in every region, i.e., crop zones. From studies in the San Francisco Peaks in Arizona emerged the system of lifezones which scientific and

agricultural research adhered to for over half a century. The biological surveys under the leadership of C. Hart Merriam suggested that temperature is the single most important factor in fixing limits beyond which particular species of plants and animals cannot go. Southern distributional limits were determined by mean temperatures during the hottest part of the summer; isotherms of 10°C, 14°C, 18°C, 22°C, 26°C became the lower, or southern, life zone boundaries. Northern, or upper altitudinal, life zone boundaries were calculated by the sum of mean daily temperatures over the growing season, using 6°C as the threshold value. What resulted were five elevational life zones corresponding to latitudinal belts delimited by regional temperatures. From subtropical to polar regions these were termed, respectively, the Austral, Transition, Canadian, Hudsonian, and Alpine Zones.

Figure 4. Distinctive zones of forest vegetation are seen along the southeast-facing slopes of the White River. They extend a vertical distance of 800 m from the river bottom to Sunrise Ridge. (See also Figures 6 and 7.)

Merriam's zonal descriptions are good generalizations for the mountains of Arizona, but what about Mount Rainier? The Transition Zone in Arizona features ponderosa pine, but around Rainier that tree is the rarest of all conifers—instead, we prefer to think of the lowest forest zone as a Western Hemlock Zone. At intermediate elevations the Canadian Zone is more accurately described in mountains of the Pacific Northwest as a Silver Fir Zone. And the Hudsonian at the highest forested elevations corresponds to the Mountain Hemlock Zone. Each zone contains numerous forest types; in fact, there are 20 major types in the park if we include subalpine parklands, and some of these have important phases (Table 1). Some forest types or phases are young, others old, but each can be recognized by a dominant tree of either the canopy (in mostly young forests) or regeneration (old forests) together with a leading plant of the understory. For convenience, the leading tree and understory species are given in the name of the type or phase. What visitors actually see in the forest landscapes of the park are not sharply defined zones of forests but mosaics or patterns involving various of these types (or their phases) at any elevation. But if Merriam's theories regarding the vertical zones of vegetation in mountains were correct, why should this be so?

The difference between theory and reality is the difference between zone and pattern. Suppose the landscape and environment around Mount Rainier consisted of the following elements:

1. The surface of the volcano is a perfect cone,
2. The soils are everywhere uniform,
3. The climate around the cone has only a vertical component of variation,
4. Along any elevational contour of the cone surface the climate is identical, and
5. The forests everywhere are all the same age and very old.

We know, of course, that none of these five conditions exists. The surface of the volcano is deeply dissected and uneven. Soils are very complex, varying in depth, texture, parent materials, degree of wetness, and so on. The various sectors of the cone present contrasting climates; for example, it might be raining at Carbon while sunny at White River. Forests of different ages have been produced by various disturbances, such as fires, mudflows, glaciers, snow avalanches, floods, etc. In effect, the landscape and landscape history at Mount Rainier are extremely complex, and the forest patterns reflect this. Although the concept of vertical zonation is useful, it is only a simplification of limited interpretive value.

Table 1. Forest types and important phases at Mount Rainier National Park. Old forests (O) are over about 250 years old; young forests (Y) are mostly less than about 250 years old. The forest types are listed in approximate order, from warm and dry environments to cold and wet environments.

Age	Approximate Forest Type and Phase	Elevational Range (in feet)
Y	DOUGLAS-FIR/STICKY LAUREL	2800-3500
Y	DOUGLAS-FIR/EVERGREEN VIOLET	2400-3500
Y	DOUGLAS-FIR/BEARGRASS	3300-4500
Y	RED ALDER/SALMONBERRY	2200-2700
O	WESTERN HEMLOCK/VANILLA LEAF	1800-2300
O	WESTERN HEMLOCK/SWORD FERN	1700-2800
O	WESTERN HEMLOCK/DEVIL'S CLUB	1700-3200
O	WESTERN HEMLOCK/SALAL	1700-3300
O	SILVER FIR/DEVIL'S CLUB	2200-4800
O	SILVER FIR/ALASKA HUCKLEBERRY	2100-4600
O	OREGON GRAPE PHASE;	2100-3500
O	STRAWBERRY-LEAF BLACKBERRY PHASE;	2800-4600
O	ALASKA YELLOW-CEDAR PHASE	3100-4200
O	SILVER FIR/FOAMFLOWER	3500-4900
Y	NOBLE FIR PHASE	3500-4900
O	SILVER FIR/SALAL	3300-4300
O	SILVER FIR/OREGON GRAPE	2600-4700
O	SILVER FIR/BEARGRASS	4100-5200
O	WESTERN HEMLOCK PHASE;	4100-4800
O	MOUNTAIN HEMLOCK PHASE	4500-5200
O	SILVER FIR/DWARF BRAMBLE	4800-5600
O	AVALANCHE FAWNLILY PHASE	4400-5500
Y	SUBALPINE FIR/VALERIAN	4800-5600
O	ALASKA YELLOW-CEDAR/OVAL-LEAF HUCKLEBERRY	3700-4900
O	SILVER FIR/RUSTY LEAF	3600-4900
O	SILVER FIR/RHODODENDRON	3600-5300
Y-O	SUBALPINE PARKLAND	5500-6100

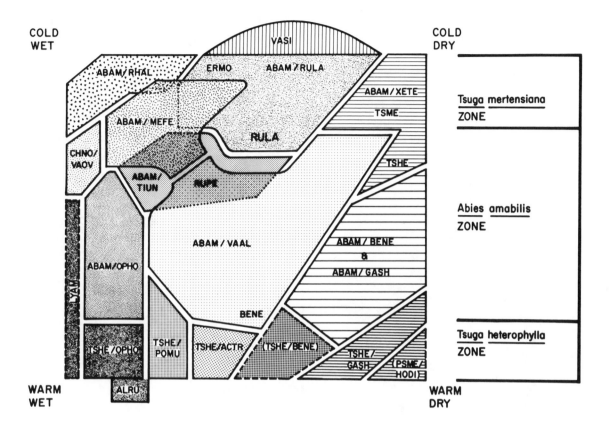

Figure 5. Generalized zones and patterns of old forests on an environmental plane representing the variations of climate at Mount Rainier. The four-letter acronyms denote the following plant species:

ABAM (*Abies amabilis*) - Pacific silver fir
ACTR (*Achlys triphylla*) - vanilla leaf
ALRU (*Alnus rubra*) - red alder
BENE (*Berberis nervosa*) - Oregon grape
CHNO (*Chamaecyparis nootkatensis*) - Alaska yellow-cedar
ERMO (*Erythronium montanum*) - avalanche lily
GASH (*Gaultheria shallon*) - salal
HODI (*Holodiscus discolor*) - oceanspray
LYAM (*Lysichitum americanum*) - skunk cabbage
MEFE (*Menziesia ferruginea*) - fool's huckleberry
OPHO (*Oplopanax horridum*) - devil's club
POMU (*Polystichum munitum*) - sword fern
PSME (*Pseudotsuga menziesii*) - Douglas-fir

RHAL (*Rhododendron albiflorum*) - Cascades azalea
RULA (*Rubus lasciococcus*) - dwarf bramble
RUPE (*Rubus pedatus*) - strawberry bramble
TIUN (*Tiarella unifoliata*) - foamflower
TSHE (*Tsuga heterophylla*) - western hemlock
TSME (*Tsuga mertensiana*) - mountain hemlock
VAAL (*Vaccinium alaskaense*) - Alaska huckleberry
VAOV (*Vaccinium ovalifolium*) - oval-leaf huckleberry
VASI (*Valeriana sitchensis*) - Sitka valerian
XETE (*Xerophyllum tenax*) - beargrass

16

Consider a more realistic generalization of forest patterns in the park. Suppose the array of forest environments can be represented by a plane whose corners are warm-wet, cold-wet, cold-dry, and warm-dry extremes of climate. Going from the bottom to the top of this plane is like passing through temperature zones, and from left to right through moisture zones. The plane contains all possible combinations of temperature and moisture of the forested region. Suppose, too, that we just consider the older forests so that patterns resulting from different ages are eliminated. Figure 5 shows how these mature or old-growth forest types are distributed over the generalized climatic plane. At the center of the plane is the SILVER FIR/ALASKA HUCKLEBERRY type, which we believe represents modal environments of the Silver Fir Zone, i.e., neither extremely wet nor dry. Another conspicuous feature of the pattern is the diagonal boundaries from warm-wet to cold-dry corners separating many of the types. These diagonals represent what ecologists call slope effects, i.e., that at any elevation, south- or west-facing slopes are warmer and drier than their opposite north- or east-facing slopes. In addition, lower slopes are usually wetter

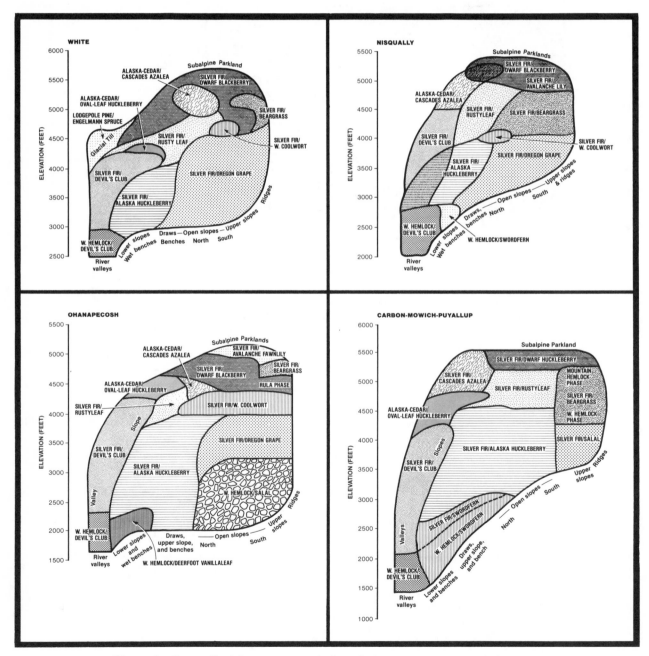

Figure 6. Generalized forest patterns in four drainage sectors around the Mount Rainier volcano.

and upper slopes and ridges are usually drier than the midslope norm. To see how this works, consider the WESTERN HEMLOCK/SALAL type which prevails on warm-dry sites at lower elevations in many areas of the park. But this type can also be found at higher elevations on south-facing (or westerly) mid and upper slopes and on ridges that are also warm-dry sites. Hence the diagonal distribution of the WESTERN HEMLOCK/SALAL type in the environmental plane. In general, whatever the climate at any elevation, the local effects of topography and soils can produce departures toward cold-wet, warm-wet, warm-dry, or cold-dry variations. These departures determine much of the forest pattern in the real landscapes of the park. And what about the vertical boundaries shown in Figure 5, especially along the wet (left) edge of the plane? These suggest that wetness itself is the prevailing determinant of forest distribution within broad elevational limits. We have already seen, for example, how the SILVER FIR/DEVIL'S CLUB type prefers saturated soils of slopes or valleys, whether at 2500 feet or 4000 feet elevation.

Alas, even the forest pattern on this generalized environmental plane is, like the Merriam zonation theory, an oversimplification. The difficulty is that each of the major watersheds radiating from the 14000+ foot mountain cone has its own distinctive climate; also, there are differences in soils and landforms from one valley to another. Patterns of forest distribution in different watersheds are illustrated in Figure 6. The shape of the overall forest area in each watershed is not rectangular, but of curvilinear form determined generally by elevational limits of the principal landform features—valleys, open slopes, ridges, benches, and draws. For example, broad forested valleys at 5000 feet elevation occur in none of the areas, although sideslopes and upland ridges are usually forested, while at lowermost elevations in the park ridgetops and upper slopes are rare. By comparing the four patterns of Figure 6, the reader can see that the distribution and assemblage of forest types are different in each valley—from Ohanapecosh, the driest, to the Carbon and Mowich, the wettest.

Theory can be matched to actuality by studying forest pattern details along trails and roads—for example, along the road from the White River Entrance Station to Sunrise Ridge (Figure 7). From bottomland, through the ribs and gullies of the glacier-

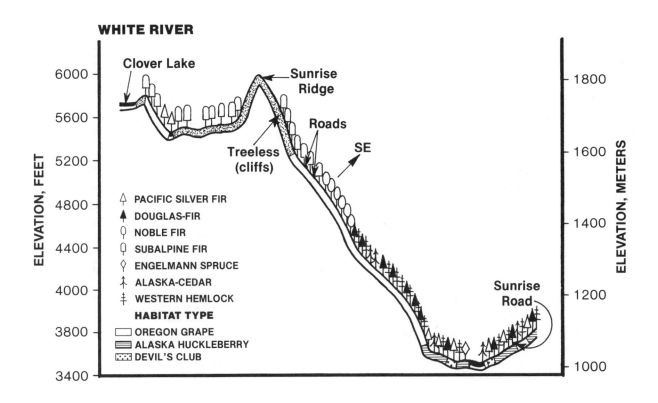

Figure 7. Forest bisect, White River.

18

carved valley wall to the uplands and ridgetops, the road traverses contrasting forest stands. We are mostly in SILVER FIR/ALASKA HUCKLEBERRY forest between the entrance station and White River bridge. Near the White River we find Alaska yellow-cedars and occasional Engelmann spruce, indicating cold airflow and other environmental features of the main drainage. Where the road crosses smaller streams or rivulets, there are stringers of SILVER FIR/DEVIL'S CLUB forest. Winding up the canyon slope, we pass through forests mostly of the SILVER FIR/OREGON GRAPE type. Western hemlock, Douglas-fir, western redcedar, and here and there a western white pine are the common trees; the understory vegetation is generally a sparse assortment of low evergreen shrubs, such as Oregon grape, pipsissewa, and several wintergreen species.

Around 4500 feet we catch sight of the bluish, bristly-rigid branches of noble fir; these are fire-initiated stands of the SILVER FIR/FOAMFLOWER type. We round the hairpin turn at 4700 feet and are suddenly amid graceful narrow spires of subalpine fir. The infrequent silver fir can be distinguished by the more fully rounded crown shape; these trees and the lush herbaceous and shrubby floras below the trees signal that we are now driving through the SUBALPINE FIR/ VALERIAN type. If the season is early, snow may yet be lingering; but it is melting fast on the southerly slopes, for this is one of the "warmest" of our high elevation forest types. Soon the forest becomes more broken by meadows; we are approaching the ridgetop and uplands of the subalpine parkland. Whitebark pine is rather common. The last several miles to the Visitor Center run through lush, herby meadows punctuated by solitary trees and small forest islands.

Another rewarding forest drive connects the Box Canyon of the Cowlitz River to the campground of the Ohanapecosh Valley (Figure 8). Near the picnic area of the Box Canyon, as well as the segment of the Wonderland Trail into Stevens Canyon, are young forests of the DOUGLAS-FIR/EVERGREEN VIOLET type. These are easily identified by the profusion of herbs—evergreen violet, bracken fern, twinflower, vanilla leaf, false solomon's seal, and many others. From Nickel Creek to the viewpoint at Backbone Ridge, the forests are only about 100 years old and mostly Douglas-fir. They are the consequence of recent fires, a phenomenon dealt with in Chapter 4. If the understory is mostly bracken fern and beargrass, then we are seeing the DOUGLAS-FIR/BEARGRASS type that is so common here.

As we round the turn of Backbone Ridge and enter the Ohanapecosh Valley, we can look across to

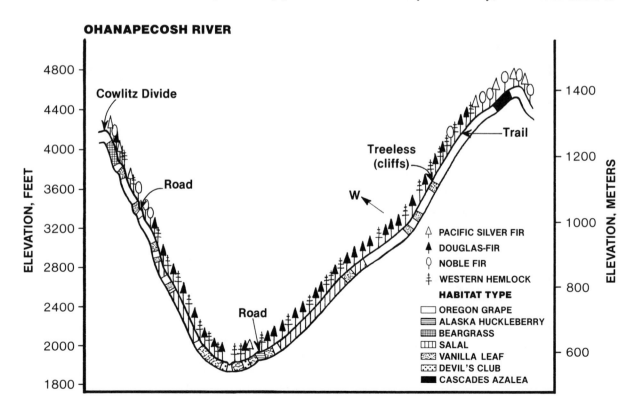

Figure 8. Forest bisect, Ohanapecosh River.

extensive slopes canopied by Douglas-fir and western hemlock. At lower elevations, these forests, with their dense understories of vine maple and salal, are the WESTERN HEMLOCK/SALAL type. At midslope is SILVER FIR/OREGON GRAPE forest, but this cannot be distinguished from our viewpoint across the valley since the dominant trees are the same as the WESTERN HEMLOCK/SALAL type. Near the ridgetop, however, we can discern bluish canopies of noble fir that indicate young forests—the NOBLE FIR phase—of the SILVER FIR/FOAMFLOWER type. Forests of the steeper canyon sideslopes along which the road passes generally mirror the zonation pattern of the opposite, west-facing slope, but are interrupted by cliffs, meadows, and rock slides.

Near the campground in the valley are mosaics of three easily distinguished forests. The wettest sites have an abundance of ferns and devil's club—the WESTERN HEMLOCK/DEVIL'S CLUB type described in Chapter 1. The driest slopes are dominated by salal, red huckleberry, and vine maple—they are the WESTERN HEMLOCK/SALAL forests, common along the Silver Falls Loop Trail. The third forest is characterized

by the strong expression of herbs (vanilla leaf, evergreen violet, silvergreen foamflower, and others); this is the WESTERN HEMLOCK/VANILLA LEAF on well-drained, moist lower slopes, draws, and terraces.

In the wet, drippy sector of the park is an interesting forested transect from Paul Peak to the ridgetop in the vicinity of Golden Lakes. The forest sequences along the south-facing slopes of Paul Peak are not unlike those of the lower Ohanapecosh Valley just described. But the lower slopes of the Mowich Valley (Figure 9) contain forests of the WESTERN HEMLOCK/SWORD FERN type not found in the drier Ohanapecosh drainages. The bottomlands of the Mowich (in the vicinity of the shelters) contain stands of SILVER FIR/DEVIL'S CLUB forest, or SILVER FIR/ALASKA HUCKLEBERRY on drier soils. Lower slopes and draws with a northerly aspect are again of WESTERN HEMLOCK/SWORD FERN vegetation, but this time with greater abundance of silver fir and mixtures of both sword fern and deer fern in contrast to this type on south-facing lower slopes across the river where only sword fern is conspicuous. Around 3600 feet the trail to Golden Lakes passes

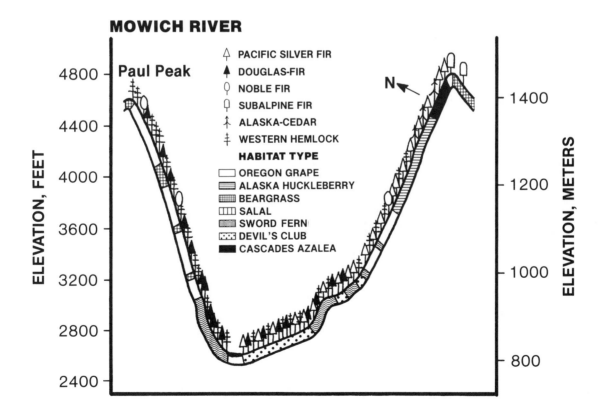

Figure 9. Forest bisect, Mowich River.

through stands dominated by western hemlock and silver fir (noble fir is occasional), but with a very sparse, almost non-existent understory flora. Infrequent sword fern, deer fern, or Alaska huckleberry hint that we are passing through habitats of SILVER FIR/ SWORD FERN or SILVER FIR/ALASKA HUCKLE-BERRY forests. We notice that plants often grow more plentifully alongside the trail. Could it be that greater light here, the result of tree removal for trail construction and maintenance, is the cause?

Gradually the understory begins to change and increase as the ridge is approached. At the higher elevations we might enter a vapor condensation zone where rising moist air cools below dewpoint. Mist and clouds obscure the canopies of silver fir, mountain hemlock, or Alaska yellow-cedar. A gentle drizzle accompanies us, and drips off the glistening foliage of rhododendron, oval-leaf huckleberry, or rusty leaf. Mounds of snowpack contribute to the cold, damp gloom of the forest, which here is the SILVER FIR/ RHODODENDRON type. At ridgetop and on slopes descending to the Golden Lakes basin the forests are very open, fire-derived SILVER FIR/BEARGRASS, featuring occasional subalpine fir and a dense ground cover of beargrass, black huckleberry, and grasses.

* * * * * * *

What began in a carpeted office as a hesitant contemplation of vast, unknown forest has ended on the Golden Lakes uplands, many footsore traverses and canopied road miles later, in a kind of celebration of diversity. From the skunk cabbage to the beargrass, from the deciduous maple to the evergreen cedar and hemlock, from the red alders of the streambanks to the fawnlilies flowering at the margins of the retreating snowpack, the forests are always changing. This diversity of forest patterns in the park, in response to the changing environments, makes the trails and roads—and the trackless wildernesses—all the more captivating. At first comes a perception of differences; next comes the dawn of understanding; and finally we experience the joy that comes with a sense of belonging. We have discovered that the forests along the lower flanks of the great volcano are a match to the patterns of color displayed in the flowering meadows above and the swirling moods of clouds, rock, and ice still higher.

Chapter 3
Intimacies

To study the forest man must climb; to study the sea, dive.

— *Marston Bates*

To inspect the forest in its third dimension, we must change scale and linger within, experiencing it as a community of myriad organisms. This is not easily done, for, as Marston Bates observed, man is a creature of the forest floor. Since we are neither subterranean nor arboreal, much of the exciting forest life escapes us. But sound and fragrance permeate the forest, and our tutored senses can perceive signals from all its tiers. Voices and moods are everywhere. In this chapter we will seek to expand our senses, forget our gravitational limitations, and step out of our tiny, personal bubbles of perception, freely circulating in forest space.

Sound and Sense

Have you ever really listened to the silence of a tall forest? I remember walking along the highway to the Ohanapecosh Ranger Station very late one dark night; the blackness was absolute, as was the total lack of sound. The forest is also silent when soft mist caresses tree canopies in early morning dimness, at midday when sunlight and shadows combine to make midday patterns across logs and moss carpets, and when snow lies deep and branches still carry the last storm's load. In any hour or season, forest silence may be accentuated by the crack of rupturing ice on a distant glacier; the sound waves approach and pass, leaving the air once again tranquil. Light makes no sound during absorption by the leaf. Water rising in tree trunks along the fine threads of xylem columns does so silently. The fungal thread penetrates moist humus; the fern releases spores; the wasp larva metamorphoses—all without fuss or fanfare. The great, interlinked machinery of the forest ecosystem pulsates, throbs, and flows soundlessly all around us. We are part of this living system; the silence engulfs us. Yet out of this great background of silence, the educated ear can distinguish differences.

I knew a biologist who claimed he could identify any forest in North America by sound and smell alone. The forests of Mount Rainier would pose no difficulty in appealing to ear and nose.

When spring snows melt along the trails in the canopied landscape, we are accompanied for miles by the "squeaky wheels" of hidden winter wrens advertising their nesting territories in the undergrowth of huckleberry and vine maple. The long-sustained, high, resonant trills of varied thrushes reach us from unseen heights of the hemlock-Douglas-fir canopy. The two tiers of sound give this forest a vertical dimension by a unique means of measure. No oak or pine forest this! Our sound space is filled by sudden arpeggios and arabesques at intermediate levels. Thrushes, chickadees, jays—or even the shrill goshawk overhead. Most startling of all, perhaps, is the loud, staccato drumming of the Williamson sapsucker that wakens us in the gloom of early dawn. These, and other animated voices of Rainier's forests, characterize and distinguish the canopied environment.

Sounds of water are nearly everywhere, inescapable. The forest around us is transferring water along a thousand pathways. Streaming fluids and vapors are esssential to forest growth. The hydrologic cycle of tall conifer forests is accompanied by sylvan music: the steady drip of foliage, rivulets of melting waters trickling down a slope or gurgling under snow, the roar and hiss of waterfalls, a gentle thud of fresh snow falling from branches, piano or forte symphonies of tumultuous whitewaters, the splash of boots along muddy trails. Such sounds are never mere noise. Noise implies annoyance, confusion, randomness; but the forest-water interaction is none of that. Why is it we can obtain a good night's rest by the sound of flowing waters, while sustained exposure to highway sounds produces a headache? Water pathways of forest landscapes issue sounds as "predictable" as cars or trucks hurrying down the freeway, but we tend to "listen to" the stream or falling droplets and to shut out the "noise" of the traffic. In the one place we are biologically and evolutionarily at home, a part of the wholeness of form and function; in the other we remain uncomfortable. We vacation to the forest to escape the technology that assaults and insults our senses. And, once here, we pause along the trail with a revived awareness of sound; from this merging of self and environment, we are given reassurance and refreshment.

Figure 10. Ohanapecosh Falls—one of a thousand aquatic pathways.

Another way of measuring the forest is by fragrance. As we emerge from car, tent, or trailer, we are suddenly engulfed by aromas that leave not the least doubt that here indeed is a forest of fir, hemlock, or cedar. These fragrances are immensely pleasing—enough so that we are willing to pay for their counterfeits in sachets and spray cans. But they are not here for our pleasure. The aromas of "freshness," of luxuriant greenery, or of hot, sunny forest clearings are complex blends of the biochemical machinery of the forest ecosystem. Our noses register only a miniscule fraction of the totality of biochemical messages. The terpenes, amber, resins, and other aromatics of wood chemistry are particularly vivid. The sharp evening drift of campfire smoke is another forest aroma we easily recall. But a host of aromas elude us, and many a rewarding one must be actively sought. The bouquet of licorice fern; the most overpowering emanations from waxy leaves of sticky laurel, especially after a fresh rain; crushed leaves of red alder; wet mosses; the reclusive, delicate fragrance of wood nymph; a sunny trailside lined with valerian and lupine; Alaska yellow-cedar foliage; wild ginger; an upwelling mist from a plunge pool. These and many, many other fragrances contribute their identity to the uniqueness of the forest. They accompany and express the myriad interactions of life within forest ecosystems.

Such forest chemistry is a system of molecular messages: "Eat me," "Leave me alone," "I taste bad," "I live here." Some of these biochemical messages make fascinating translations. Take the case of certain forest floor orchids. One kind of bee and only one can serve as a pollinating agent for these orchids. The individual orchids, however, are infrequent and scattered. Guiding the bees over the long distances between one plant and the next are aromatic molecules that issue from the flowers' nectaries. Again, it is odor that guides male moths to the unfertilized female; she issues a specific chemical from a complex family of chemicals known as pheromones.

A nest of yellow jackets hidden in the forest litter is identified to foraging members of the colony by pheromones coming from their queen. Her message is so specific that the foraging wasp will never be deceived by the pheromones of a queen from another colony. For the yellow jackets, each pheromone is an exact address.

Certain fungi, among them the famous truffle, fruit below ground. Their spores cannot be carried by the wind, but the fruits are edible to forest inhabitants such as rodents. The spores pass through the intestinal tract to be distributed and, eventually, to germinate in the droppings of these animals. But how are these below-ground fungi found? By scent.

The tar-like pungence of sticky laurel leaves announces their unpalatability to browsing deer or elk. Certain aromatic chemicals of conifer needles, known as terpenoids, inhibit fungal and bacterial growth and prevent grazing by many foliage eaters. The musk of the deer gives some kind of danger or alarm message. Need we mention the skunk? And on and on.

These chemical pathways are metabolic interactions of the living forest. A few of these can titillate our sense of smell. By intruding our noses into these pathways, we can enjoy and appreciate some of the complexities and mysteries of the forest. Why is this bracket fungus so perfumed? Whom is it beckoning, whom is it warning away? What goes on inside the punky log factory that sends forth such earthy aromas? What kind of flies are attracted to the putrid fragrance of the spadix of skunk cabbage? What purposes do the fruity-musty glands of rusty leaf serve?

The sounds and fragrances that reach us transcend space. From a fixed point on the forest floor we can measure the forest, appreciate its ethereal dimensions. Sight is unnecessary. In the following passages we return to the visual world, but with the resolve not to neglect the other sensory aspects of forest structure and function.

Tall Canopies

Look up. A canopied universe is overhead. High-rise dwellings occupied by strange forms and a myriad of hidden organisms. The treetops, we see, are all individually shaped. There are narrow, pointed crowns of true firs, droopy twigs and foliage of Alaska yellow-cedar, or perhaps horizontal sprays of the fern-like greenery of western redcedar. We see densely foliated, whorled branches of western or mountain hemlocks. Some of the older trees have rounded or broken tops, or missing branches within the crown. Tier after tier of foliage rises upward; our necks stretch and ache. It's hard to appreciate a subject so remote, so we'll ascend into the canopy where things can be viewed more closely and comfortably.

Here's a tall, old Douglas-fir; it must be about 250 feet high. Up we go! The first living limb is about 81 feet above the ground. A fan-shaped array of secondary branches and twigs displays foliage in a kind of horizontal plane. Strange and colorful growths stretch along the main limb and branches. There are gray, pale green, yellowish, and even bluish forms. These are the mosses, liverworts, and lichens. As we

24

levitate upward we enter a peculiar realm of shape and structure. A sense of arboreal unreality closes about us as we lose sight of the forest floor now some 130 feet below. We notice that this 450-year-old Douglas-fir bears the scars and individuality of old age. Its canopy geometry is highly irregular. Some limbs are 66 feet long; others extend only a foot or so from the trunk. Vertical gaps separate one tier of branches from the next. Some branches are dead; others, still alive, are displayed on only one side of the tree. The main stem itself leans somewhat to the west. Our curiosity is intense, so here at 130 feet we stop and let our sight pass along a single large limb extending horizontally on the east side of the trunk.

Botanists have found about 200 different kinds of plants growing on the tall conifers of the Pacific Northwest. Such plants growing on other plants are called epiphytes. The algae are a group of chlorophyll-bearing plants with simple tissues that do not form roots, stems, or leaves, and may even exist as simple cells or strings of cells. Fungi are also simple plants whose filamentous hyphae lack chlorophyll and sometimes entwine themselves into specialized structures, popularly known as mushrooms, whose function is the production of microscopic spores that can germinate into new plants. The liverworts are simple green plants that are flat and usually bilaterally symmetrical with sex organs on the dorsal surface and numerous threadlike structures called rhizoids on the lower surface. They are fork-branched or ribbon-like plants with little distinction between leaf and stem. Most of us are more familiar with mosses. Mosses appear leafy along a main stem, and can be either erect or creeping. Lichens are plants whose body, called a thallus, consists of structured arrangements of fungal hyphae that envelop algal cells—one of the many examples of a mutual accommodation of life known as symbiosis. All of these organisms comprise a diverse

Figure 11. Bearded limbs of mountain hemlock.

botany up here. The algae and fungi are hard to see, but with a hand lens we can visit communities dominated by mosses, liverworts, and lichens.

Here at dizzying heights we discover a sharp habitat differentiation on the upper and lower surfaces of the Douglas-fir limb. The upper side of the limb is covered with green stringers of *Hypnum circinale* and erect tufts of *Dicranum*, both mosses. The grayish, intricately branched and shrub-like body of *Sphaerophorus globosus*, a lichen, is common; we saw this on the trunk, too. One of the most common plants is a showy lichen whose unusual shape and bright green color (when wet) is seen along limbs and well into the branchlets at distal ends of this branch system. It's one of the "lung" lichens, whose thallus is divided into a reticulate system of ridges and cavities suggesting lung tissue. With the lens we can see that the ruffled margins of the thallus are frilled with tiny, leaf-like lobules. Most of the algal cells that give this lichen its green color belong to the group of green algae, but colonies of the blue-green algae, *Nostoc*, also grow in specialized structures within the thallus. *Nostoc* can convert atmospheric nitrogen into organic forms of nitrogen. The lichen *Lobaria oregana* is really a symbiotic arrangement of two algae and a fungus.

Many other plants are found in the moss-lichen community on the upper surface of the main limb, a dazzling display of a mini-plant world. The branch supports about a pound and a half of the larger epiphytes; their foliar surface has a total area of about 17 square feet! We need a specialist to identify them all, but can marvel at the differences in form and color. On the drier, lower side of the limb we find a less complex community containing the common leafy liverwort, *Scapania bolanderi*, growing along the smooth bark surface. Also a bluish, powdery mold; this is the lichen, *Lepraria membranacea*.

The lichens are most spectacular; the fungal body, or thallus, determines the growth form of the organism. The remarkable variety of form is reflected in the plethora of botanical terms such as sorediate, crustose, foliose, squamulose, and fruticose. These are names that botanists use to classify the growth forms of lichens. The upper surface of the limb is dominated by foliose and fruticose lichens; the lower by sorediate and crustose forms.

Lichens are extremely hardy. They are a major plant group of arctic tundras, snow and ice zones of mountain summits, and bare rock surfaces in climates ranging from deserts and tropics to polar regions. They withstand extremes of dessication and temperature beyond the tolerances of all other plant life except bacteria and certain algae. Lichens form crusts on desert and arctic soils; indeed, they seem to thrive in severe climates where most other plants cannot even exist. Most of their mineral nutrition is extracted from traces found in rainfall or runoff. If the air becomes too "enriched" by oxides of sulphur or nitrogen and other pollutants, many lichen species will die. Judging from the wealth of lichens in this canopy, the air at Mount Rainier is pure and clean.

What about the microclimate of this limb? Dominance by mosses and lichens suggests a rather extreme environment ... cold, drippy winters and maybe some tundra-like periods of snow or ice; summers when the limb or branches are as dry as a desert soil. The further out on the branch or the closer to the tree summit, the more extreme become the variations in microclimate. In tropical or subtropical forests, where climates are more uniform and mild, the canopy epiphytes frequently include orchids, bromeliads (the pineapple family), and ferns as well as mosses and lichens. Here at Rainier a few ferns are occasionally epiphytic, but the vascular plants generally find the arboreal environment too harsh.

Let's go higher. *Lobaria oregana* continues to be the dominant organism on limbs and twigs, but not on the trunk. From about 160 feet to very near the crown top, we find the yellowish, pendulous lichen, *Alectoria sarmentosa*, in beard-like drapery on the trunk. In higher elevation forests various species of *Alectoria* are among the most conspicuous lichens hanging on limbs, branches, and trunks. Our particular canopy is getting drier and is subject to wider variations in temperature and light as we ascend. Mosses are not quite as abundant now. But the fruticose *Lobaria* is still plentiful, and as we progress outward we notice an increasing abundance of various crustose lichens, especially on the smaller branchlets and twigs. The outer envelope of the tree canopy at this height is a virtual desert. If this were the tropics, we might find species of cactus in the comparable position. In the Mount Rainier forest, however, the branchlets support only the hardiest of crustose lichens. The mosses, with their higher moisture requirements, have disappeared. Life has been reduced to its simplest, enduring forms.

We reach the summit of the tree at 246 feet and look down. Below is a sea of green. About 60 million Douglas-fir needles are displayed on this particular tree. An additional foliar surface of significance is represented by the grays, pale greens, yellow-greens, and deep green forms of epiphytic mosses and lichens. This single tree is a kind of outlandish modern art sculpture with millions of components designed to capture light. The collective surface area of all the needles is about seven-tenths of an acre, or

Figure 12. Vine maple glowing in the soft filtered sunlight of the forest interior.

30,500 square feet. The surface area of the epiphytes growing on the tree is probably at least as great, but has not been measured because of the complexity of their form and distribution. As light passes through this magnificent sculpture below us, it is rapidly attenuated. A "beam" of light striking any surface within the crown volume will be partly absorbed, partly transmitted, and partly reflected. The probability of striking a photosynthetic surface is very high; this crown structure is extremely efficient in harvesting light. The light scattered at mid- and lower-crown levels can be used by liverworts, mosses, and lichens at the crown's interior. This impressive plant assemblage testifies that radiant energy is too valuable to be wasted on non-photosynthetic bark or branches! By the time the light has filtered below the lowermost limb, it has been reduced to ten percent or less of its original level.

We now perceive the plant life's strategy for survival in the canopy. The higher in the canopy a plant can survive, the better its chances to obtain vital radiant energy for photosynthesis. Most vascular plants are earthbound and must rely on their root systems for nutrients and water. They can elevate their leaves only so far and hence contend for whatever leftover light is available in the forest interior. Even the needles of the tallest conifers are earthbound. Should the water and nutrient conduits be severed, the needles die. If plants can elevate themselves on the structures of other rooted plants, however, they can display their own photosynthetic apparatus in a more favorable light environment. In the tropics, vines, lianas, and epiphytes make use of the elevated structures of other plants. In the Pacific Northwest forests, only those plants that have totally severed their requirements for soil-supplied water and nutrients have succeeded as epiphytes. They pay a high price for this independence and photosynthetic advantage. They must withstand severe dessication at various times during the year, be able to obtain nutrients from the atmosphere or bark substrate, and be able to tolerate the hot and cold temperature extremes of exposed arboreal perches.

Epiphytic plant communities are not parasitic. The lichens and mosses merely use the trunk, limbs, and branchlets as perching platforms. Most of their mineral nutrition comes, as mentioned, from the slight quantities dissolved in rainwater or flowing down the trunk or branches. Wherever there is enough unused energy (in this case, light from the sun) in conjunction with life-sustaining nutrients, some peculiarly adapted life form moves in and starts the business of storing energy and nutrients in its structure. A number of species that associate with the blue-green algae meet their nitrogen requirements by biochemical fixation of atmospheric nitrogen.

On some trees, to be sure, we might find mistletoe, which is parasitic and uses the tree as a nutrient- and water-supplying host. But the moss-liverwort-lichen assemblages are free-living up here. As absolute and complete apartment dwellers, they don't ever have to descend to the ground floor for groceries. We look upon them with respect.

The animal communities of the tall canopies are just as remarkable. Mammals include the silver-haired bat, several kinds of myotis bats, the northern flying squirrel, and chickarees. The marten, a large predator of the weasel family, gracefully and swiftly uses the limbs and branches as hunting routes, but hunts on the ground as well. Both the northern flying squirrel and chickaree are considered arboreal since they reproduce in canopy nests.

The foraging tactics of these and other mammals can be thought of as partitioning the forest into stratified tiers. When snow covers the ground, the northern flying squirrel dines on epiphytic lichens; but at other times it searches the forest floor humus for hidden fungi that are fruiting below ground. The chickaree is also a two-tiered feeder. It will clip the cones from the uppermost canopy to obtain nutritious conifer seeds, and much of its time is spent on the ground searching (by smell) for fungi fruiting below ground. The squirrel is active at night, the chickaree by day. This difference in time of activity for ground-level foraging minimizes competitive contact and partitions the available fungal flora as a food source.

Complex food webs exist in the canopy. The Douglas-fir needles are eaten by species of sawflies, scales, mealy bugs, aphids, and other invertebrates. Bacteria and fungi help decompose the older needles and are themselves food for many species of mites, various fly larvae, and springtails. Other canopy mites and spiders feed upon these and other invertebrates. Many insects live as adults in high canopies, but as larval stages in soil or fresh water. These include certain mosquitoes, true bugs, beetles, caddis flies, and stoneflies. The myotis bats materializing at dusk and flitting erratically in open spaces between one canopy and the next are searching by radar for these adult canopy insects.

The food webs of canopies can be divided into nine functional groups: grazing vertebrates (such as the chickaree), grazing insects, sucking insects, seed and cone insects, parasitic and predatory invertebrates, predatory vertebrates (such as bats and a number of birds), omnivorous birds, and nest predators (such as the marten). The fact that there may be around 450 species of canopy invertebrates suggests the complexity of the "who eats whom" relationships.

The bird life up here is probably best known, thanks to binoculars, patience, and sore necks. The canopy is the foraging stratum for cedar waxwings, red crossbills, ruby and golden-crowned kinglets, Townsend's and hermit warblers, and pine siskins. The varied and Swainson's thrushes singing from canopy heights actually do most of their feeding at ground level. The dietary preferences of many species vary seasonally. The availability of food sources determines the diet of such omnivores as blue grouse, band-tailed pigeon, Clark's nutcracker, the common raven, and chestnut-backed chickadees.

It is the pileated woodpecker, however, that recalls to me the images of forest primeval. The dead limbs of venerable trees are nesting sites; these are hidden within the foliage of the surrounding live branches at great heights. The pileated woodpecker is shy; we're lucky to get a glimpse of this giant black bird with its flashing red crest, most likely while it is foraging almost at ground level among dead snags and logs. Lucky, too, if we hear its tattooing drum from some resonant dead trunk within its territory.

Raptors such as the northern spotted owl, Cooper's and sharp-shinned hawks, and the goshawk all make use of the canopy for nesting, observation, and vantage points to swoop upon prey. The spotted owl is one of the terrors of the chickaree population, and small hawks, such as the sharp-shinned hawk, are adroit at pursuing other birds through the labyrinth of crown branches and foliage.

Because of its inaccessibility, the canopy's food web is still relatively unknown. The faunas of moss-lichen communities are a mystery. What kind of snails feed upon these thalloid foods, and who eats or parasitizes them? How are the larval or adult stages of insects synchronized to flushes of needle growth? What are some of the search or evasion mechanisms of the predatory-prey relationships of the canopy? How do woodpeckers manage to detect the larvae of insects under the bark? How do the warblers skillfully hide their nests from raids by jays and martens? The plant and animal life of the canopy will continue to capture the imagination and attention of biologists for years to come.

Big Trees

"Holy cow! Look at this whopper!"
Admiring the trees is one of the most enjoy-

able pastimes at Mount Rainier. The roads and trails through old-growth stands are ennobled by these great specimens. The big trees leave no doubt that they have character and personality. We gaze upon their stems with awe and fascination, and feel great respect for such dignity.

Sometimes, when confronted by a big tree, our deep inner feelings emerge as rather childish remarks. "Here's a really big dude!" Dude, indeed. If the tree could rebuke us, it might comment on the triviality of our expression in the presence of wisdom and endurance of great age. But what can one do when faced with such splendid members of the plant kingdom? A great artist or poet might extract the quintessential personality of the big tree, but we're just ordinary people. Even more futile is to sum up the massive form of the tree by the triviality of a single measurement. Yet such a monumental oversimplification is precisely our way of expressing tree size: by its diameter at breast height (or, even more denigrating, "dbh"). The great mountain hemlock before us is silently admired for a moment or two. Then, in discharge of our pent-up emotions, one of us will walk around the stem with a tape. "Fifty-five inches." The catharsis performed, we are now comfortable to proceed along the trail.

Now it's no easy matter to measure a large tree's diameter. Look at that large Douglas-fir, for example. Around its base is a huge, conical mound that formed over the centuries by gradual enlargement of the root crown, soil displacement from increasing stem girth, and the accumulations of bark and other detritus sloughed from the stem and crown. The platy, yellowish bark of the Douglas-fir has been buried by as much as three to six feet of the mound. Foresters think of "breast height" as 55 inches above the ground, but where is ground level from which to measure? We climb the root mound and struggle around the tree with our tape. We're probably somewhere between six and ten feet above the "ground" where the tree might have started out as a seedling seven centuries ago.

It is even more delicate to measure a big tree on a steep slope. The uphill side of the stem has large accumulations of debris, while the downhill side may be at or below the original ground level of the seedling. As a compromise, one stands at the midslope side of the tree with tape at breast height and then starts around the stem. What a journey this is! The horizontal plane is tilted by the angle of the slope, so that the actual distance around the tree is about 33 feet. And that is one of the most difficult and hazardous terrains I know of. On the downhill side, the tape is about three feet over our head; on the uphill, it's at our

Figure 13. The author poses in front of eight-hundred-year-old Douglas-fir along the East Side Trail.

feet in order to keep the measurement as horizontal as possible. After all that exertion and an expletive or two, as vine maple or devil's club impedes our progress, we no longer care about the poetry, or lack of it, that the measurement summarizes. We're damn glad to still be alive!

Nevertheless, the big trees are impressively beautiful. The population of big trees at Mount Rainier National Park is rivalled in the Northwest only in or at Olympic National Park. Mount Rainier, in terms of the large areas of its old-growth forest, is the "big tree park." Everyone coming here has heard of, or visited, the Grove of the Patriarchs. The western redcedars there are huge and spectacular. But did you realize that similar big specimens—not only of the cedar, but also Douglas-fir, western hemlock, mountain hemlock, silver fir, and Alaska yellow-cedar—are found all along the Ohanapecosh River and its tributaries? When I think of large trees and ancient forests, I identify first and foremost the East Side Trail. If you really want to savor the moods and impressions given by large trees and old-growth stands, then start at Cayuse Pass and hike down the trail all the way to the Grove. You'll never forget the experience.

Big trees can also be viewed by car. The best drive, weather permitting, is the canopied old growth of the Carbon River valley. The forest there is the WESTERN HEMLOCK/DEVIL'S CLUB type, featuring large Douglas-fir, western hemlock, western redcedar, and, at the very start of the drive, Sitka spruce. The road along the Nisqually River is also through big-tree landscapes. From the entrance station to Paradise, we can see large specimens of nearly all the conifers. Look for the big nobles at Nahunta Falls, Alaska yellow-cedar at Narada Falls, mountain hemlock and subalpine fir from Narada Falls on up to Paradise. You might have fun putting a tape measure to the big nobles at Nahunta Falls; these trees are about 350 years old.

Why are the trees so big? This seemingly trivial question is actually quite profound. Sure, they're big because they are old. But you cannot tell a tree's age by its size alone. The thousand-year-old Douglas-firs at Cougar Rocks campground are neither very tall nor of great diameter. In fact, some 650- to 700-year-old Douglas-firs nearby are nearly twice the diameter because they occur in more favorable habitat. One of the biggest Douglas-firs measures 110 inches at "breast height" diameter, and is just a little over 500 years old. It's in the Carbon River valley.

At the cold, snowy climates of the high elevations, the relationship between age and size is even more tenuous. An Alaska yellow-cedar in the White River Campground is over 900 years old and not very big. It looks like one of the "poles" of the understory. A mountain hemlock that luckily escaped the harsh rigors of youth—snow burial and understory suppression—is a massive specimen at 300 years while its neighbor, equally as massive, exceeds 600 years.

Age is only a partial explanation for size. Clearly the habitat in which the tree grows also affects its height and diameter growth. Still a third factor is the microclimate around the individual tree. Was it shaded and suppressed or open grown? Are the roots restricted to cold, saturated soils or deep, well-drained and warmer soils? What is the competition from neighboring trees?

Why are the biggest trees found in the Pacific Northwest and not Arizona or Montana? There must be something about this moist, maritime climate that favors massiveness. Let's delve more deeply into the subject. As we are often uncomfortably aware, there are plenty of wet, drippy or snowy days at Mount Rainier. But in late June and the following summer months there are dry periods. Day after day of warm, even hot, temperatures, little rain, and low humidities. During these periods, the trees do not find conditions all that favorable for photosynthesis. The ensuing moisture stress sharply reduces the gas exchange properties of the foliage (the "stomata" or tiny pores in the leaves close) and photosynthesis stops.

During the warmer growing seasons in Rainier, the rainfall is unfortunately reduced (dry summer climates). By late June, a Douglas-fir about 260 feet tall, with a foliage mass of about 770 pounds, transpires about 560 quarts of water per day. It gets this water from the soil reservoir, but cannot replenish its depleted canopy water as fast as it is evaporated while photosynthesis is taking place. Water stress occurs, the stomata of the leaves close, and photosynthesis ceases. Hence, diurnal changes in tree moisture stress during the spring and summer months limit photosynthesis to only a few hours in the morning, when both light and favorable water supplies occur. Here then, is that marvelous and efficient light-harvesting canopy that we visited in the previous section—and the whole apparatus is shut down for much of the summer day because of moisture stress!

What does this have to do with massive stems? A tree stem has two parts to its woody mass: heartwood and sapwood. The latter is especially important, for its living xylem strands carry the water upward. The greater the cross-sectional area of sapwood, the more water can be delivered to the canopy. The larger the city, the larger in diameter are its water mains. If the crown is to carry 60 million

Figure 14. Big trees and old growth near Chenuis Falls (western hemlock/sword fern forest).

needles, the stem better be big. A 260-foot Douglas-fir stem is like a giant saguaro cactus. Its sapwood at early dawn, before photosynthesis begins, may hold as much as 1,140 gallons, or 3.4 tons, of water. This large reservoir in the plumbing system of a big tree serves to dampen the diurnal change in plant moisture stress. By drawing upon sapwood water, photosynthesis can be prolonged further into the summer day. This added daily increment of energy harvest by photosynthesis is a considerable gain when summed over all the days of the year, provided other conditions for photosynthesis (light, temperature, and nutrient supply) are also favorable. Large stems act as water storing organs; they shorten the pathway of water to the crown, facilitate greater flow volume, lengthen the daily photosynthetic interval, and permit trees to bear large masses and surface areas of foliage. We perceive those big stems with new admiration.

But why are Douglas-fir trees in Arizona and Montana not equal in size at equivalent ages? A partial answer is that the optimal size and configuration of the plumbing system is conditioned by climate. A tree of the dimension of one of those Douglas-firs along the Ohanapecosh River would quickly die in the more arid climates of Arizona and Montana. There simply is not enough soil water to recharge the stem reservoir again and again if specimens in those states were to have such dimensions. Evaporative losses from voluminous crowns would be excessive. Precipitation is too low to replenish the proportionate quantity of water that would be needed from the soil. So the trees there have shorter, smaller crowns, and their stems are not nearly so massive in old age. In order to build bigger stems, a tree must pay a respiratory cost; so why build a big reservoir when it cannot be filled?

The big trees at Mount Rainier are ever a source of wonderment. I like the upper Laughingwater Creek Trail all the more because of its huge Alaska yellow-cedar and silver fir. The Mowich River valley contains some big western redcedars and Douglas-firs that I'd like to get close to. I can see their massive crowns from various overlooks along the Wonderland Trail. I know of a single, large noble fir not far from Ipsut Pass—it's right along the trail. There are also two or three places in the hinterlands where I think I've seen the biggest mountain hemlocks in the world. I've never degraded them or myself by measuring them, but like to think that perhaps they are the largest. The American penchant for records, for the biggest and the best, for pursuit of the tallest and most perfectly formed, or the largest diameter is well satisfied in the Rainier forest landscape. We approach the next curve in the road or trail ever hopeful to come across another big tree.

Mossy Rocks and Wet Cliffs

Near the start of the Silver Falls Loop Trail stands a huge, angular boulder. It is well above the rushing stream and near the edge of the valley. Ages ago, the boulder must have broken away from the cliffs of the Ohanapecosh Formation, a greenish-gray sandstone that forms the steep walls of this valley. Now it rests, seemingly content, within a tall pole forest of Douglas-fir and western hemlock. The uneven terrain across which the trail meanders is covered with red huckleberry and salal. The understory is heavily shaded. The boulder itself is just alongside the trail. It's about ten feet high, though I've never measured it and it doesn't matter.

What catches my fancy about this particular boulder is the extravagant verdure of its vegetation. The rock is softly clothed in exquisite greenery so that not a trace of its mineralogy can be seen. Its steep rock face has that most beautifully textured of all cosmetics: fuzzy mosses. Gently arching fronds of licorice fern outline the boulder's profile above me.

There are only three elements to this sculpture: the rock, the mosses, and the ferns. The simplicity of form, texture, and color are perfect. I cannot imagine the slightest rearrangement; to attempt this would produce flaws.

What's more, this display of nature's art belongs right here and nowhere else. The mossy boulder is at its best against the blurred background of tall columnar stems and shadows of the forest floor. The salal provides a restful buffer that binds sculpture and surrounding forest into the same creative continuum. This gem of the forest interior becomes the focus for the entire beauty of the Ohanapecosh forest. I am comfortable with its size and scale so that my proximity to the boulder is an entry into this esthetic continuum of the forest. Waves of empathy hold me as motionless as the curved fronds. I cannot recall how long I lingered here, nor what, if anything, broke the spell. Perhaps as mortal, imperfect beings, people can enjoy only limited exposure to perfection. But as I continue along the trail I am aware of being refreshed. Somehow I am a better person. Life seems very beautiful.

Silver Falls is another world; it cannot be described adequately. As it was in my encounter with the mossy rock, so again I have the feeling that man should not linger very long. The ground trembles and froths. The full motion and volume of the Ohanapecosh River is both awesome and frightening. Most people, myself included, gape at the sheer power and the sense of timelessness of its descending turbulence.

Figure 15. Draperies of vegetation on cliffs near Silver Falls.

But while many are held transfixed by the motion and energy of the falls, my attention centers on a different subject: the botany of wet cliffs.

On both sides of the narrow gorge are draperies of vegetation. While the thoughts of other visitors swirl and eddy with the green current, I marvel at the robustness of the large serviceberry displaying its white flowers with fine indifference to the motion beneath. The serviceberry is actually quite common in these forests, but deer and elk browse it so much that it rarely achieves full stature and unsullied form. No animal can reach it here! Other cliff shrubs above the gorge are Douglas maple and Sitka alder. This alder is somewhat out of place, for the common alder along this stretch of the Ohanapecosh River is red alder. Lovely tall groves of red alder can be seen, for example, near the Grove of the Patriarchs. But here, its branches moving in the downdraft of air propelled by the turbulence of the water, is Sitka alder, a plant normally found in higher, colder elevations. The drainage of cold, moist air in this gorge is doubtless the most important feature of this environment. Still other cliff-clinging shrubs are salal, red and Alaska huckleberries, several species of low brambles, wood rose, and yew.

Numerous flowering herbs also adorn the cliffs. The weeping saxifrage and alumroot are common cliff inhabitants of shaded, wet places. In addition, we can find woodrush, fragrant bedstraw, woodland beardtongue, foamflower, evergreen violet, thimbleberry, and twinflower. Such a cool, shaded microhabitat would be unimaginable without graceful ferns. At Silver Falls we see a dwarf variety of the common sword fern, often found, as well, on rocky rubble throughout the Rainier forest landscape. Licorice fern and fragile fern complete the fern roll call. The delicate, almost transparent fronds of fragile fern recall memories of other wet cliffs I have seen in different parts of the world. It can be found on seepy ledges of otherwise arid mountains of the Southwest, or on wet streamside banks in eastern deciduous forests. I have seen fragile fern in tall eucalyptus forests on the mountaintops of Victoria, Australia—a part of the wet rock flora of that cool, maritime climate. I share secrets with the fragile fern; we both know the friendliness and solitude of wet cliffs in different parts of the world. I hope to come across it again, somewhere, sometime.

Most of the greenness of the cliffs at Silver Falls is due to mosses. Among the many species, two are especially conspicuous. Perhaps the most spectacular is the "stepladder moss" with red stems and distinct tiers of decorative foliage. Botanists call it

Hylocomium splendens. It forms locally dominant layers on various ledge and rock faces here. The other, *Rhytidiopsis robusta*, makes carpets of interwoven strands of yellowish-green, leafy stems. The cliffs at Silver Falls have a great range of moisture and wetness, and this helps determine which mosses are where. Without attempting to render identifications on all the species, we can nevertheless study the diversity of green form from place to place as the microenvironment changes. At dry overhangs along the trail, only the hardiest mosses remain; as the dryness increases deeper into the overhang, mosses disappear, and we see blotches of a bluish or whitish, powdery "mold." Haven't we seen this before? Yes, on the underside of limbs in the Douglas-fir canopy! It's the sorediate lichen, *Lepraria*.

But back to mosses. On sunny exposed rocks near the top of the cliffs are erect, tufted mosses equipped to endure long periods of dessication. These belong to the genus *Racomitrium*. A minutely tufted cushion of moss about an inch in diameter catches my eye. The dry leaf tips give a silvery sheen to the tuft. Another old friend, *Grimmia*; a dry rock inhabitant throughout North America, as well as Africa and the southeastern Pacific. I first discovered *Grimmia* on hot, granitic rocks in the foothills of the Colorado Front Range.

I'm suddenly jolted out of the world of the hand lens.

Here I am in this swirling, tumultuous, roaring environment of Silver Falls, and my botanical reminiscences have transported me to Colorado. And why am I thinking about hot, sunny rocks, when a few minutes ago the sight of Sitka alder took me to the cold, misty climates of the high Cascades? What is more disparate than Sitka alder and *Grimmia* growing almost side by side? Whoever said that the botany of these cliffs would be dull! The perpetual motion of water is no less profound than the spectrum of botanical disarray on these rocks. Fortunately there is no need to bring order out of chaos; I am free simply to recognize and revel in this incredible diversity of microhabitat.

In desultory manner I continue botanizing. Here's another woodland beardtongue growing from a mossy crevice. The plant so nearly resembles Oregon grape that it usually is overlooked. Its disguise is betrayed in August when racemes of purple flowers are displayed. Since the stiff, holly-like leaves of Oregon grape are mostly left alone by deer and elk, the occasional presence of the more palatable beardtongue often goes unnoticed. This is a good example of adaptive mimicry among plants; in the animal kingdom, mimicry is a fascinating device used by prey and predator alike. Beardtongue has copied a page from the evolutionary book of predator-prey search and escape strategies.

On another portion of the wet cliff I see the large thallus of a lichen. The lushness of mosses here suggests this part of the wall to be rather wet. The thallus is bright green after rain and steely gray when dry; its flat surface is smooth and punctuated by black dots. This is the foliose lichen, *Peltigera aphthosa*, and it is common here. The green color is provided by cells of a green alga under the upper surface of the fungal thallus, while the black dots are specialized structures where cells of a blue-green alga, *Nostoc*, occur. We found a similar symbiotic arrangement on some of the lichens in the tree canopies, too. Since *Nostoc* can convert gaseous atmospheric nitrogen to plant-available ammonia and nitrate forms, the *Peltigera* has its own built-in fertilizer factory!

I walk to the bridge and look upstream. Violent flumes surge up from plunge pools, and the lower rock walls are always wet. It's hard to believe that even here there are plants finding congenial substrate. Probably algae and aquatic mosses, but of course it's too dangerous to find out. Besides, there is such a wealth of life along the trail where viewing is safe, why bother elsewhere? On these walls there will always be another discovery, another hidden recess to peer into, another recollection. I'll never know all the botany here. I doubt that anyone will.

Plants Without Chlorophyll

In the poor illumination of the forest floor, green plants compete fiercely for available light. Under dense tree canopies of some of the drier sites at Mount Rainier, there may be almost no understory greenery at all, except perhaps mosses. The reduced light supply, in combination with deficiencies of moisture or nutrients, has curtailed populations of green vascular plants. This vegetation sparsity reveals a sterile brown carpet of forest litter and downed logs, but the appearance of sterility is deceptive. Nowhere are some of the major processes associated with forest ecosystems more active. Nor is it for lack of an energy supply that vascular plant growth is so poorly expressed. The organic residues of the forest floor comprise a vast pool of chemical energy that powers decomposer processes and detrital food webs. The molecular transformations linking one form of life to another are so complex that, by contrast, the chemical wisdom of the petrochemical industry might seem like a first-grade primer. And nothing reveals the mutual

interactions of forest life quite so eloquently as the vascular plants without chlorophyll.

One day, I was surprised to discover in the lonesomeness of this brown world the beautiful pink racemes of one of Mount Rainier's wintergreen plants, *Pyrola asarifolia*. The plant was in vigorous, healthy flower but lacked any leaves whatsoever. I knew it as *Pyrola asarifolia* only because other plants nearby were of the normal, fully-leaved green forms. How could a plant carry on its critical flowering and fruiting functions without the carbohydrate supply furnished by green leaves? This wintergreen plant was no longer struggling with the light problem of this shadowy place. Its merry flowers were evidence enough that green leaves were no longer required. But why not?

Plants at Mount Rainier that have lost their photosynthetic function are usually in the heath and orchid families. The phantom orchid is white throughout; spotting one of these is a rare privilege. The most common achlorophyllous orchids are the coralroots, which usually are seen in clusters in the litter environment. The western coralroot has on its flowering corolla a "spur" that is suffused with pink or red, and the spotted coralroot is noted by the wine-red spots that dot the otherwise white spur. The heath family includes candy stick, with its white and pink striped stem; pinesap and the waxy white Indian pipe, both with drooping flower stalks, often clustered or congested stems; pinedrops, a tall yellow to red-brown plant with erect stems; and gnome plant, a rare recluse whose flowers are crowded into a short terminal spike. The leaves of each of these species are reduced to functionless scales. The plants seem to have only one remaining function: to produce flowers and seeds. All are quite comfortable in the detrital understory, often where their photosynthetic relatives can no longer survive.

For a long time, botanists thought these plants were directly parasitic upon other green plants. Parasitic plants penetrate the living host tissue with specialized structures known as haustoria and obtain their carbohydrate supply from the photosynthetic products of the host. But these heaths and orchids have no haustoria and no direct contact with other green plants. Instead, they form an association with various fungi on the forest floor. Fungi are among the most common organisms of the soil. The numerous species include some of the major decomposers of organic matter. Fungi perfuse detrital space in long threadlike growths, called hyphae, collectively forming mycelium—a subterranean structure that almost literally envelops the earth. Since these are microscopic, we see some of the fungi only when their

Figure 16. Wintergreen (Pyrola asarifolia) without leaves.

hyphae are massed into specialized reproductive structures we know as mushrooms.

The fungi succeed in soil because their source of metabolic energy is mostly the chemical energy of the detritus. Some species are wood decay organisms; others decompose conifer needles, dead roots, bark flakes, deciduous leaves, or other plant debris. Certain fungi are coprophilous—they grow only on the manure of animals. Other kinds of fungi form associations with roots of living plants. For example, all coniferous trees exhibit a kind of fungal association called mycorrhizae—networks of hyphae forming small balls of tissue along the smaller absorbent rootlets of the trees. Mycorrhizae play a major role in tree nutrient uptake and are especially well developed in soils low in nitrogen or phosphorus. On fertile soils conifers can grow well without mycorrhizal roots, but on most soils of the Cascades, foresters have learned that the proper association of a tree species with its particular fungal organisms improves seedling survival and tree growth.

But let's return to the modest pale orchids and heaths. As mentioned, they are not parasites, but compensate for their inability to manufacture their own carbohydrate supply by developing a symbiotic relationship with various fungi on the forest floor. Botanists refer to this functional association as mycotrophy, literally "fungus nutrition." With some plants, this association is a matter of circumstance. Where the light supply is adequate, green leaves provide carbohydrates; but when photosynthesis cannot keep up with the plant's demands, then mycotrophy develops. Two interesting examples illustrate this. The small wintergreen (*Pryola picta*) can be found with individuals ranging from green, independent plants through semi-dependent plants with small green leaves, to plants with no leaves at all and root systems thoroughly infested with fungi. Yet all these individuals are freely interfertile members of the same genetic population. The second example from the orchid family shows the reverse trend. Young plants of the twayblade genus (*Listera*) depend totally on mycotrophic nutrition for seedling growth, but as green leaves develop the mycorrhizal fungi gradually disappear.

These examples suggest a mechanism by which mycotrophic dependency could have evolved within groups of vascular plants. Light-starved green plants of the forest understory are weakened because of the low levels of carbohydrates. Their root tissues become susceptible to parasitism by species of fungi. The hyphae either penetrate the plant tissue (as they do in orchids, for example) or merely surround the rootlets (as with most heaths) in order to obtain the metabolic products of the weakened plants. Some plant individuals, however, are able to reverse this action and assimilate the carbohydrates or other metabolic products of the invading fungus. In some orchids, for example, the penetrating hyphae are eventually digested and further spread of the fungus through the host plant is checked by production of compounds such as orchinol. Whatever the mechanism, these individuals are able to check the complete infection of the fungus and derive sufficient nutritional supplement from the fungus to complete seed production. Other plants of the parasitized population may die. This differential survival under a selective mechanism of a host-parasite relationship could bring about the evolution of mycotrophic symbiosis.

As dependency upon fungi increases to offset reduced photosynthetic capacity, the roots of vascular plants progress through a variety of forms. Candy sticks have tiny, non-green leaves but an extensive fibrous root system. The rattlesnake plantain (*Goodyera oblongifolia*) has a small rosette of evergreen leaves (although their variegated appearance results from absence of chlorophyll along the veins) and underground fleshy stems (rhizomes) with roots developed at the stem nodes. The roots, or both roots and rhizomes, are strongly infested with fungi. The plantain has a little of both autotrophic and mycotrophic nutrition. The coralroots, despite their name, have no roots, for only the below-ground rhizomes remain. This is a remarkable structure since it permits the plant to spread vegetatively (coralroots are usually seen in clusters) and store food that can be used for flowering. This rhizome is strongly mycotrophic. The extreme of root abortion is found in the pinedrops, Indian pipe, and pinesap. The masses of hyphae are so closely woven around the conducting tissues of these plants that they form a root ball that entirely shields the plants from contact with soil, organic matter, or other green plants. These plants have not only lost their leaves, but their roots as well! The important thing, of course, is that they are quite successful in reproducing by means of flower and seed production in an environment where other adaptations that are more conventional among flowering plants no longer work.

What about the fungal associates of this remarkable partnership? We know less about their taxonomy and degree of dependency or about the metabolic advantages they derive from the association. Some of the fungi belong to the bolete family (*Boletaceae*), which often forms mycorrhizal partnerships with trees as well. Some fungi, such as *Armillaria mellea*, are capable of obtaining nutrients and carbohydrates from a variety of green plants, including some

38

Figure 17. Indian pipe in the shaded, detrital environment of the forest floor.

conifers. When scientists injected radioactive carbon (in the form of glucose) into spruce and pines, they found that the pinesap plants growing among their roots also became radioactive. A mycorrhizal fungus provides the link between the two plants. Further evidence of this was found when radioactive phosphorus injected into the pinesap soon appeared in nearby mycorrhizal trees. What started as simple wonderment about the survival of non-green vascular plants on the shaded forest floor led to discovery of a three-way involvement of a green tree and fungus as well. The fungal component, however, may be less obligatory in some cases; nutrients and possibly carbohydrates might be obtained directly from the organic matter of the soil.

Another pattern of symbiosis can involve certain fungi that form mycorrhizal associations with other green vascular plants, whether or not achlorophyllous vascular plants are present. The two-part arrangement becomes tripartite only if seeds of the non-green plant are carried into the area.

These pale plants of the forest floor always catch my attention when I'm passing through dense forests on dry midslopes or elsewhere. Flowering defiantly, they symbolize the tenacity of life. To them nothing about the dark understory or detrital realm of the forest floor is, as I might otherwise perceive it, harsh and forbidding. No, indeed; they are quite at home and doing well. They glory in the darkness, and there's no competition from struggling green plants. Perhaps that obscure mushroom fruiting not too far away is the secret of this plant's success. Most certainly these little vascular plants have invaded the domain of the fungi by forming partnerships with them. Is this any less remarkable than the fungi invading the domain of the green plant world by forming partnerships with algae and thriving as lichens in the tall canopy? The ecology of the forest is a thousand tales of plants and animals living in a marvelously complex interaction with one another.

Beneath Our Feet

Nothing was particularly different about this forest along Fryingpan Creek, except its location. Don and I were about seven miles west-northwest of the volcano's summit. The Douglas-firs here had been growing for about 730 years. Some large western hemlocks were here, too, and because of the cold-air drainage along the creek, occasional Alaska yellow-cedars were seen. The forest was approaching almost complete dominance by silver fir. Their graceful spires reached far into the canopy, and their saplings were everywhere.

Don was our soils expert this summer, and we were here to find out what kind of soil existed at this location. Our first problem was to decide where to dig, for we knew that soils changed quickly from one place to another. The forest gave us no hint. Both of us had seen the SILVER FIR/ALASKA HUCKLEBERRY forest type again and again throughout the summer. The rather uniform cover of shrubs—Alaska, oval-leaf, and black huckleberries—gave no suggestion that one particular site might be different from any other as far as the soils were concerned. The very ordinariness of this forest along Fryingpan Creek lulled us into complacency. It had all the appearances of just another dig.

But there is nothing ordinary about the forests of Mount Rainier, or their soils.

We chose a rather level terrace not far from the creek and began digging. At the end of minutes we were pumping adrenalin furiously, and not just because of exertion. It took about a half hour to expose the soil profile, but we had no awareness of time. Both Don and I knew we had made an exciting discovery. We sat at the edge of the soil pit and viewed with exhilaration the profile we had exposed. Not a word was spoken; we just looked. Later this soil would be analyzed carefully by scientists at Washington State University; right now, however, we were admiring our discovery and feeling very excited.

In the stratigraphy of soil layers we could read the present and ancient history of this forest. We saw a chronicle of changing landscapes that took us back more than 4,000 years. Stupendous volcanic eruptions and terrifying rains of ash were here revealed, not just from the giant volcano a few miles away, but from Mount St. Helens, too. Extinct forests and ancient fires. Floods. The chronicle had many gaps, to be sure; the soil would have to be analyzed in detail before the story could be unraveled. Both of us were aware of our limitations at this moment, our inability to understand all we were seeing. But we were certain that when the complete soil profile had been meticulously scrutinized by soil scientists, geologists and biologists, an exciting tale would be unfolded.

We would like to share with our readers an interpretive history of the forests of Fryingpan Creek as revealed by this soil. Beginning at the top, we will work our way backward through time. Our passage will be marked in metric measures; that's how Don and I described the profile.

0-12 Centimeters: The Present Forest

The soil surface is mantled with organic

40

matter derived mostly as litterfall. Freshly fallen needles, cones, twigs, branches, flakes of bark, and other detritus can easily be identified. Coniferous forests like this one produce about 5,300 pounds per acre of litter every year. Were this to accumulate year after year, our stand would be buried under almost 50 feet of debris, not including the coarse material—especially those "down logs" which might total another 340 tons per acre. Our profile, however, reveals only a thin veneer, perhaps three-quarters of an inch thick, of the current year's litterfall. Below this is a progressive decomposition and fragmentation of organic matter, so that by the 4.7-inch depth only the most resistant humus remains. The lower humus layer is quite black; we can no longer tell whether this amorphous duff originated as needles, cones, or what.

Organic layers of the forest floor are very complicated recycling and waste-disposal factories. Howard Ensign Evans calls them "cities of the soil."

There may be as many as 350,000 mites and over one million nematodes in a square yard. A freshly fallen Douglas-fir log here may contain, among other forms of life, the following insect groups: more than 18 species of phloem feeders, 18 or more species of heartwood and sapwood feeders, at least 22 species of fungus eaters, and 46 species of parasites and predators. Nothing is "dead" about the microcosm of forest floor humus. Organic matter is being processed by dissolvers, shredders, choppers, and grinders. A kind of steady-state dynamics has been achieved whereby yearly inputs of fresh litter are balanced by losses of the finer sizes of organic matter due to the respiratory metabolism of detritus food webs.

A conspicuous feature of the humus layer just above the mineral soil is the abundance of fine roots. Perhaps we expected the absorbent tree roots to be deeper. Because it takes a vertical space of 130 to 260 feet, more or less, to accommodate the green fabric of

Figure 18. The whitish ash of Layer W is a conspicuous feature of the soil throughout much of Mount Rainier's forested region.

the forest, we might guess that the rooting volumes must also be very deep. Not so; about 90 percent of the underground forest biomass is within a yard of the surface, and nearly all of the fine, absorbent roots are within the upper 25 centimeters of the soil. It makes sense, too, that most of the nutrient-absorbing functions of the trees and shrubs take place in humus layers where the nutrients are most concentrated. The black duff is permeated by root networks and the fungi that often associate with them in a complex, symbiotic arrangement known as mycorrhizae.

We could linger for hours in the biological world of the forest floor humus, with its microflora and hidden faunas. This really is one of the most important parts of the total forest ecosystem. We'll revisit it in Chapter 8; right now, however, the remainder of the soil profile beckons.

12-20 Centimeters: The Present Forest

Abruptly the black humus ends; we now see a grayish sand. Don suggests I look at this horizon carefully. I note plenty of fine woody roots, but little else except the sand. At the interface between the humus and mineral soil is a thin, almost continuous mat of fine roots and mycorrhizae. This net of roots and fungi is a kind of screen taking up nutrients leaching through the humus layers above. The horizon consists of single-grained mineral sands giving a whitish cast that contrasts strikingly with the black humus above. Geologists who studied the mineralogy of these sands have traced their origins to an eruption of Mount St. Helens. From radiocarbon dates of charcoal both above and below this layer, they determined that the eruption took place about 460 years ago (from a base date of 1980). Because of the white color of the sand, it was named, for convenience, Layer W.

The forest at Fryingpan Creek was about 300 years old when Mount St. Helens erupted. I could imagine that day. Perhaps the air was filled with sulphurous smells. On the other hand, since that volcano is about 50 miles away, maybe those odors didn't get this far. In any case, however, I'll wager that no birds were singing while this rain of sand was sifting through the canopy! An eerie whiteness might have settled on the branches and leaves, and when it was all over, a shallow layer of volcanic "snow" covered everything on the forest floor. If the sun could penetrate the yellowish haze of the finest volcanic particles still suspended in the atmosphere, it must have illuminated the forest interior with a surrealistic glow and reflection. This forest might have been part of Middle Earth.

"Do you still not see?" Don's voice jerked me back to reality. I looked around. Everything about this forest had a healthy, reassuring green. "Immediately above Layer W." I assumed an eyeball to eyeball position with the sand grains. Now I could see it: there were not one, but two separate colors and textures. The two layers were in direct contact but unmixed. The very top of the mineral horizon had a thin, discontinuous covering of very fine, dark gray sand; below lay a medium-grained sand of lighter value. The upper layer was also a volcanic ash—the "Post-W" deposit. Was this a final puff from Mount St. Helens before she became quiescent? Maybe a final residual fallout after the heavier sands of the W had already emplaced? Did St. Helens erupt more than once that year, or several times within a short span of years? We don't know.

20-24 Centimeters: Recent Forests Including the Present

The sand grains continue, but are now distinctly darker. We are looking at the upper part of a soil that was buried by the Layer W deposit. Some of the sand grains are coated with humus; others show clean mineral faces. Also, small flecks of charcoal contribute to the darker coloration. Fine and medium-sized roots are common.

Several complexities about this horizon have not been answered by soil scientists. The mineralogy itself differs from that of Layer W, although the source of this volcanic deposit is probably also St. Helens. The biochemistry of this horizon is complex, because both humus-coated and clean-grained soil mineral particles occur. Maybe the humus remains from the time the soil was buried, while the clean-grained sands result from leaching under the present forest and soil environment. The charcoal reveals an ancient fire or fires, for this substance is inert in soil and produced only by fire (Chapter 4). The present forest of Fryingpan Creek doubtless originated after a fire; it succeeded an earlier forest whose only remains are the charcoal flecks.

24-27 Centimeters: Present and Ancient Forests

Abruptly we come to a brown horizon of considerable depth. There are not very many fine roots here. Probing around with the soil knife, we find roots mostly of larger diameters than those above. The most outstanding feature, however, is the gravelly texture. Mount Rainier erupted several times about 2,000 to 2,500 years ago. These were explosive events with

42

masses of hot rocks avalanching down the volcano's cone and blobs of red-hot lava thrown from the vent. Large amounts of pumice also were ejected; we're looking at these pumice deposits. Geologists call this Layer C and have given it a radiocarbon date of about 2,200 years B.P. (before the present).

Don divided Layer C into two soil horizons. He identified the upper as a buried illuvial horizon. The pumice gravels and sands are coated with a thin layer of iron oxides, which give a reddish cast to this part of the profile. The iron oxides are products of soil weathering mostly in horizons above. The rates and intensities of mineral weathering, which form the oxides, depend on the chemistry of the minerals, the organic environment of the soil, and the climate. In ash soils of the higher elevation forests of Mount Rainier, for example, are thick, hard, and impermeable "iron pan" horizons that represent the extremes of the weathering and precipitation processes in cold, wet climates. We suspect the presence of iron pan soils when trails are especially soggy. Water can no longer percolate vertically because iron oxides clog the soil pores. Thus, water moves laterally above the iron pan and creates saturated horizons above, through which our boots slog. The Fryingpan Creek profile, however, was no such problem. The iron coatings are thin, and the soil remains well-drained.

The lower horizon of Layer C does not show iron stains. It looks just as the raw pumice must have appeared when it fell from the sky and cooled. The sequence of vertical horizons to this depth illustrates a suite of what soil scientists call the A-B-C horizons. The profile was formed under the influence of the present forest but was complicated by several ash burials. In addition, some features appear to be carry-overs from older soil profiles and former forests before burial.

27-69 Centimeters: Ancient Forests

Below the brown and iron-stained pumices of Mount Rainier is a dark soil layer banded with light-colored and finer textured minerals. The darker minerals are from a volcanic eruption of unknown source. The lighter bands are other pumice deposits, or a sequence of deposits, that have again been identified with Mount St. Helens. It's called Layer P. This whole mineral mass is a remnant of very old soil. We were unable to find any enriched organic matter, accumulations of iron, or other features associated with soil development. Yet surely a forest grew here about 3,000 years ago when this ash fell. We suspect that the minerals we are seeing lay deep within the soil of those

forests, for the mineral chemistry is as unaltered as the day they settled from the sky. By the time Mount Rainier was showering hot ashes and fiery blobs over the valley, this old soil was already truncated by erosion. Today this material is again too deep in the profile to be much affected by the influences of the existing forest. To be sure, a few roots can be seen, but nearly all of the biological processes related to soil formation are going on in the horizons above.

69-89 Centimeters: Ancient Forests

We have come to a layer of coarse, bright yellow sand. Don recalls seeing this same yellow sand as a surficial deposit in the northwest sector of the park, while in Nisqually Valley it is located just below Layer W. But here it is deep within the profile. This is our fourth pumice deposit that has been traced to eruption of Mount St. Helens. It's known as Layer Y after its yellowish color. The sand grains are quite even in size, but vary from whitish to orange. The entire horizon has a uniform appearance that conveys to me a sense of freshness and cleanness. The thickness of Layer Y at this site along Fryingpan Creek is unusual. Since our site is on the valley floor, it is possible that the sands washed in from the surrounding slopes after they were deposited over the entire landscape between 3,250 and 4,000 years ago. Possibly these sands were redeposited by floodwaters receding from this river terrace. Maybe there was just an unusually heavy airfall here from some atmospheric eddy brought about by the turbulence of St. Helens' eruption. These sands, however, will not reveal their secrets today.

Like the horizon just above, Layer Y seems to have existed deep within the soil of the forest it once supported. We are now contemplating forests around 4,000 or more years ago. Fossil soil profiles of such antiquity can be quite well preserved, however, when buried deeply and located on rather stable geomorphic surfaces. But in the uniform sands before us we see absolutely no horizon differentiation. It is probable, considering the time span involved, that forest growth came and went to the tune of fires, floods, landslides, mudflows, and even glacial advances. Soils are equally ephemeral: a stable soil under one set of conditions becomes an erosional soil under another. Whatever surface soil once existed in those times has long since disappeared, and only the deeper remnants of the unweathered soil profile remain. Considering the position in the landscape at our profile site, floodwater could be the agent of erosion. If water could carry the sands in, it could also carry them away.

And the forest, too, vanished without a trace.

Don and I looked upon our saga of forests that came and disappeared and parent materials that fell from the sky when the earth gods were angered. Compressed into an earthen rainbow at our feet was an explosive and resplendent history of the past 4,000 years. Don has classified the kind of soils where layers of volcanic pumice deposits are found as "tephra soils." The term "tephra" refers to fragmental volcanic particles exploded from a volcanic vent and carried through the air. Tephra soils are common in these forests, but the sequence of layers differs from place to place. The whitish or yellowish sands can be seen throughout the park along trails and roadcuts. From the most violent of origins, great forests have arisen ... and vanished. What of these forests today? Will another great flood level them and remove their upper soil? Will Rainier or St. Helens again bury them under ash? Will another great fire sweep through? Will they disappear without a trace, or leave a message in the soil for posterity?

Who knows? Perhaps man is the greatest of geological phenomena. He can darken the air in as drastic a manner as the volcanoes: witness the view of Mount Rainier from Seattle. He can change the periodicities of fire and maybe even modify the climates under which the Fryingpan Glacier will advance or retreat.

But as the two of us contemplate the story of our soil profile, we are reassured. The forests have endured. They have healed the scarred landscapes again and again. Life is incredibly persistent. The many intimacies of the forest attest to the varieties of adaptation over centuries of adversity. In the final analysis, it is the process of evolution that is most wonderful. Perhaps man has introduced terrific new selective pressures by his modification of the environment. But somehow we feel that this great forest, under the shadow of Rainier's mighty vent, has the adaptive machinery to continue on for centuries to come.

44

Figure 19. The tall pole forests near Ohanapecosh campground were born in fire holocausts about 250 years ago.

Chapter 4
Fires *(or Playing Sherlock Holmes)*

Rain-soaked, fog-shrouded, the stately forests of Mount Rainier seem to range from damp to sopping. How hard it is to imagine them on fire. Yet evidences of fire are everywhere; from green valleys to subalpine ridges, from the Mowich to the Ohanapecosh. Not just recent fires such as Shriner Peak and the oft-burned upper Cowlitz valley, but burns of antiquity long before James Vancouver ever set his eyes on the Northwest coast...not just piddling local blazes, but massive holocausts that must have gone on for days and weeks...not once, but repeatedly.

To look at the evidence, let's go for a walk through the forest, taking with us a spade, a hand lens, and an increment borer. Where? Doesn't matter—the evidence is everywhere, the fires were everywhere. How about the Laughingwater Creek Trail?

The path enters tall forests carpeted by mosses and shrubs. The trees are festooned with lichens and mosses. A varied thrush is singing above. But we're looking for charcoal...

We examine the litter on the forest floor. The aromas of moist, fermenting humus greet us. Bits of conifer needles and small, broken twigs and cone scales dribble between our fingers. But no charcoal. Immediately below the humus we encounter moist, whitish sands of a recent volcanic deposit...the "Tephra layer W" that geologists have identified as coming from a Mount St. Helens eruption about 460 years ago. But still no charcoal. Let's try another site.

Again we examine the litter without luck. Carefully we lift and remove the forest floor litter as a mat above the Tephra W. A small blackish fleck catches our eye. Charcoal? To test, we rub the fleck across the palm of our hand. Charcoal leaves a black smear, but this fleck does not. It turns out to be just a partially rotted piece of root bark. Another fleck, another smear test. Our skepticism mounts. Then a third try and this time a comet-like smear appears on our palm from a particle about the size of a pin head lying on the surface of the W. This is definitely charcoal. Very well, but one raindrop hardly constitutes a storm. Where shall we look next?

If a hot fire swept through here centuries ago, it might have charred the stems of some trees. Since charcoal is biologically inert (it's merely elemental carbon), it might persist as a crust on logs fallen after the fire. Our eyes make out the gentle forms of old

logs hidden under the carpet of moss and litter. With the spade we expose a section of punky log, a bright reddish orange. The best place to find the former bark surface is where the log contacts the mineral soil. No black crust there. But the entire stem might not have been charred, just the basal part where this alleged fire was hottest. We see the faint mound of the root crown where soil was thrown up as this tree toppled over centuries ago. We expose a couple of sections near this base. No charcoal. Is there something wrong with our logic? Perhaps there was no fire here after all.

Suddenly one of our digging companions shouts. Where her log is resting on the surface of the whitish sand is a charcoal crust black as sin. We poke around the area another quarter hour and tally a grand total of five charcoal findings. Since we accept the fact that charcoal comes from fire, we're convinced... or are we? It's still incredible that fire could have swept up this damp area of Laughingwater Creek.

We continue up the trail, noticing that most of the Douglas-firs are about the same size. They're big—about two or three feet in diameter near the ground—but not so large that the increment borer cannot reach the center. The coring tool permits us to remove a tiny rod of wood from the tree. If our luck or aim is good, that rod or core will contain the center-most tree ring, a tiny dot representing the uppermost shoot when this 200-foot giant was a sapling of breast height. We twist the borer ever deeper into the stem of one of the biggest Douglas-firs, selected because we think it might be one of the oldest trees in the stand. The cutting edge of the tip bites through decades of living sapwood and then more decades of non-living heartwood. The wood is sound and sturdy through the entire section—no sign of rot. Still more decades in, and at last we think we have reached the center. The extractor is inserted down the tube of the borer, and the woody core is pulled out. With fascination we watch the tree rings—some wide, some narrow—slip by as the core is drawn out. With a hand lens, one of us sits on a sunny log next to the trail and begins to count rings.

A tree's age can be determined by the following formula: Age = number of counted rings + number of growing years to reach the height at which the borer was inserted + number of tree rings between the innermost ring on the core and the central (year 1) pith.

*Figure 20.
Increment coring
a large western
white pine.*

If we're skilled enough to reach the center of the stem, the last term of the formula will be zero, and our age estimate will be more precise. While the count is being performed, the others are guessing. "Seven hundred years." "Less than two hundred." "Eleven hundred, betcha a dollar." The counter looks up; the forest silence is deafening. "Two hundred and fourteen rings." With corrections added on for age to core height (20 years assumed in this case) and two more

years because we just barely missed the center (we could tell by the curvature of the rings at the distal end of the core), the specimen comes out to 236 years, more or less. We realize that maybe this stand isn't so "primeval" after all; in fact, it is relatively young! To be sure, we check three other large Douglas-fir trees along the path, each of them, we hope, older than the one before. On one tree we actually hit the center ring. After an hour or so, to say nothing of arms tired from twisting the increment borer into very resistant stems and then twisting it out again, we have the following ages: 236, 214, 237, 195. One of us is inspired to try the instrument on a large western hemlock. With beginner's luck and a careful count, we add the age 201 to our collection.

As we continue up Laughingwater Creek Trail, we become aware of the numerous similar-sized stems of Douglas-fir which, we now realize, are between about 200 and 250 years of age. A stump made a few years ago by the trail crew permits another ring count without the agony of twisting the borer. The stump is a Douglas-fir that, when cut, was of a size similar to the others. The count falls within the 200-250 year range. By now it is clear that we are passing through an "even-aged" stand of Douglas-fir. There are no young Douglas-fir—no seedlings, saplings, or small poles—below the overstory canopy; and we encounter no trees older than about 250 years. Such Douglas-fir forests are known to occur in the Pacific Northwest after some kind of holocaust. This tree species regenerates well in open areas. For example, it has naturally regenerated on many of the clearcut areas outside the park. Evidently, about two and a half centuries ago, conditions were just right for extensive Douglas-fir establishment along this three-mile stretch of trail. What kind of natural catastrophe eliminated all trees older than about 250 years and produced openings in which Douglas-fir seedlings could take hold? What gave rise around 1725 to a Douglas-fir establishment episode that appears to have lasted for 40 or 50 years?

Forest fires have taken place in the Pacific Northwest on both large and small scales. About 2,000 square miles of Douglas-fir forest originated from the legendary "big fire" of the Cowlitz around 1800. Closer to Mount Rainier were the "great burns" of the upper Cowlitz Valley in 1841 and 1856 and reburns at intervals around 1886-1889. The forests of Backbone Ridge can be dated to these periods of fire by the age of some of the older Douglas-fir trees—100 to 120 years. The charred snags of the former forest still exist—and these were big trees that were killed.

Large portions of the Cascades burned in 1868-1869, including the Bear Prairie area on the road from Ashford to Packwood. A part of Paradise Valley burned in August 1891 when Len Longmire avenged himself for stings from a yellow jacket colony. When he set a match to their nest, he also ignited the forest.

The year 1902 saw more than a hundred fires in western Oregon and Washington. Skies turned yellowish-acrid and the sun was hazy week after week in late August and September when low humidity and strong east winds fanned clearing fires into blazes, including the greatest human tragedy (which resulted, among other things, in at least 35 human lives lost), the Yacholt Burn.

The Tillamook Burn of coastal Oregon began 14 August 1933 and could not be extinguished by man. Ten days later, low humidity and stiff east winds blew the fire into a holocaust that consumed 240,000 acres of forest in 20 hours. At one time 3,000 men were on the fire line, but it remained for a wet blanket of fog rolling in from the Pacific to finally put it out.

These are some of the recent fires that are remembered and documented. But some of the fires that burned in prehistoric times were more than a match for the burns of record. When Plummer inventoried the Mount Rainier Forest Reserve in the 1890s, he noted that most of the major valleys exhibited young forests on recently burned lands. He also saw "ancient burns" memorialized by many of the larger, old-growth forest stands. Traces of those burns still remained, he wrote, but since the lands had long since been restocked by trees grown to large sizes, Plummer did not refer to them as burns.

This even-aged stand along the Laughingwater could represent restocking by Douglas-fir after one or more of these "ancient burns." The ages of the oldest trees suggest that the fire took place about 1700. This predates the "big fire" of the Cowlitz lowlands by a century.

We must remember that the oldest trees do not give the date of the disturbance, since several years may elapse before trees begin to invade. (We'll have more to say about this in the next chapter.) We do know that some kind of extensive forest disturbance took place earlier than 250 years ago. Our evidence so far is:

1) some charcoal,
2) an even-aged Douglas-fir stand, and
3) no trees older than 250 years.

Could some other hypothesis fit these facts?

The trail angles up a very steep slope. The scarp-like surface and the very uneven topography that we pass through is a huge landslide. Did this landslide level the forest around 1700? Indeed, the extensive area and massive volumes of rock carried in this landslide not only leveled the existing forest, but probably annihilated and buried it! But an intact surficial deposit of Tephra W appears on the top of this landslide, so we know the last major landslide was more than 460 years ago. It is highly improbable that it would take over two centuries for trees to become reestablished here. No, whatever event destroyed the previous forest is more recent than the landslide.

A mudflow? We're too far away and too sheltered from any mudflows originating on the volcanic dome of Mount Rainier. Could insect epidemics have wiped out the forests? Extensive defoliations by species such as the spruce budworm and tree-kills by bark beetles, especially of Douglas-fir and western white pine, do take place in Northwest conifer forests now and then. But foresters know of no insects that wipe out all species of trees in a forest stand simultaneously.

Any other alternatives? How about a destructive wind that could blow down the big trees regardless of whether they were Douglas-fir, western hemlock, or pine? Windthrow damage is not uncommon. It could create large areas favorable to a new generation of forest. But it leaves evidence in the form of many logs facing roughly the same direction—and it does not leave charcoal. It's possible that fire took hold and burned all the blown-over trees after they dried out, but then we're back again to the fire hypothesis, only this time after wind destruction. "Maybe the charcoal we found near the start of the trail was just a local fire—say lightning striking a tree and burning a few nearby acres?" So we again search for charcoal and find it here and there, usually between the Tephra W and the forest litter layer.

A short distance farther, the path passes a small pond. The gentle repose of this lovely pond— the "eye of the landscape" in Thoreau's words—takes our mind away from fires, and makes us aware that it's lunchtime. What a beautiful spot, and just look at those big trees along the edge of the pond. Hold it! We take a second look at those trees, and lunch is momentarily forgotten. Those characters are BIG. Some are three to four feet in diameter. We look around. There are still some of the 200- to 250-year-old sizes along the trail just passed, but beyond the pond the Douglas-firs are bigger and so too are some of the western hemlocks.

The fire must have ended about here, for what confronts us near this pond has the appearance of a real forest primeval. Over lunch we speculate on the ages of the Douglas-fir and enjoy the beauty of the surroundings. There's lots of Alaska huckleberry in the understory, whereas salal was the dominant shrub of the forest in which we had spent the morning. Could the fire have swept through the drier salal-type forest and burned out when it encountered the wetter environment of a huckleberry-type forest? We also notice greater densities of saplings and seedlings of silver fir, and a few specimens which are tallish poles. Some of the other plants near our lunch site are vine maple (we had been seeing that all morning), pipsissewa, bunch-berry, beadlily, and big huckleberry.

We core one of the big trees after lunch. It takes the caloric equivalent of about a package of M&M's to put that instrument as far into the Douglas-fir stem as it can go. Some tree rings of the extracted core are so close together that even with an eight-power hand lens they are almost impossible to discern. It takes about ten minutes to count rings, and over some portions of the core the count is pretty crude. There are about 570 rings, and after corrections are added for age to core height and additional rings to the center, we estimate the specimen to be around 640 to 660 years old. There is no doubt—we have entered another age class of forest.

Monster trees accompany our continued walk up the trail. Pleasing, too, is the cheerful, musical sound for which Laughingwater Creek is so well named. About a mile and a half beyond the pond the trail levels off into a high, wide valley. Big, big trees. Occasional Douglas-fir, but even silver fir is among the canopy dominants. Still lots of Alaska huckleberry in the understory, but vine maple seems to have dropped out. We begin to encounter some large specimens of Alaska yellow-cedar. Is it possible that this forest was ever burned? It would have to have been a truly ancient burn! Let's look for charcoal.

Our search in the litter, under punky old logs, at the surface of the Tephra W, and within the sandy layer of the W deposit all prove futile. No charcoal is to be found. Then we start to think about this. Suppose the forest is 640 to 660 years old. Didn't we mention that the Tephra W was a volcanic ash fallout from Mount St. Helens 460 years ago? That ash must have rained through these trees and covered the old forest floor. If there's any charcoal, it would be below the Tephra W. Give me that shovel!

And so it is. Not everywhere, for the centuries that elapsed between the old fire and the fallout of Tephra W have seen much removal by erosion of the fire's charcoal deposits. We know from our morning's experience not to expect charcoal everywhere, and now we are pursuing fires another four centuries backward in time. We do, however, discover charcoal at widespread locations throughout this old-growth forest. Usually such discovery is accompanied by relatively intact "fossil" soil profiles buried below the Tephra W layer. This is an important observation, for we have to make sure that any charcoal we find was not washed in from another location. We have to discount some charcoal findings in soils that are clearly mixed or disturbed, for these may have originated at some other upslope location. But large logs usually remain where they fall, and charcoal crusts on

Figure 21. A rare survivor of at least one fire holocaust: this charred Douglas-fir is several centuries older than the other trees along the Silver Falls Loop Trail.

some of these are our best evidence that fire took place at this location.

Before we turn to go back, a few more large trees are cored and aged. Each turns out to be over 600 years old. As with the morning's walk, this Douglas-fir population is essentially even-aged. But the afternoon's forests are much older, and the error associated with our age determinations is greater. Natural mortality over the centuries has slowly reduced the Douglas-fir population, and other tree species more tolerant of the cool, shaded forest environment, such as western hemlock and silver fir, are gradually replacing Douglas-fir.

The evidence of prehistoric fires is rather obscure along Laughingwater Creek Trail, but not in other areas of the Ohanapecosh drainage system. The forest between the Ohanapecosh Campground and Silver Falls is an example. Hikers along the Silver Falls Loop Trail pass through 200- to 250-year-old stands of Douglas-fir, western hemlock, and occasional noble fir. Charcoal can be found on the forest floor. We have reason to believe that the same fire that swept up the Laughingwater also burned in the Ohanapecosh Valley. The forest age structures are statistically the same at the two locations, which suggests that either the same fire event gave rise to both forests or several fires were so close in time as to be indistinguishable. But a very sharp-eyed observer can find something along the Silver Falls Loop Trail that eluded us along Laughingwater Creek: the rare survivors of that fiery holocaust. These surviving trees give a mute but impressive testimony of our fire hypothesis. Their trunks are sometimes charred to about 40 feet above the ground. The heat of the blaze did not, however, ignite the crown; had it done so, the tree would have been killed.

We can conjure up that fire—over 250 years ago—whipping up the valley and the mountain slopes, flames roaring sometimes hundreds of feet above the ground; a "killer" crown fire that crackled and seared its path from one tree top to the next with lethal swiftness. But there were a few "holes" in the forest canopy that could not carry the fire; instead, the fire passed at ground level with blistering heat. Smaller trees were quickly killed, but a few of the larger Douglas-fir had thick enough layers of insulative bark that the extreme ambient temperatures could not penetrate and kill the living cambial tissue. Scorching these trees, the fire passed and these trees lived on.

Charred, 450-year-old Douglas-firs are thinly scattered along the Ohanapecosh Valley from the park boundary to about Silver Falls. Their sites on valley bottom or lower slopes indicate these tree individuals were somewhat sheltered from fire effects; perhaps the microsite was slightly wetter. Although never common, in the aggregate this surviving Douglas-fir population gives us some idea of the forest that was burned. At least we know that many of them are around 450 years old. And since these trees are rather widespread along the valley, something other than local disturbance created the forest openings in which these Douglas-firs grew. If fire could sweep into the Ohanapecosh Valley once, it could do so again.

Old-growth forests whose tree populations reveal multiple disturbances are not uncommon in the park. Sometimes we can find charcoal both above and below the Tephra W, attesting to multiple fires. A two-aged population of Douglas-fir can be found, for example, along the southeast-facing slopes of Deer Creek, where both 600- to 700-year and 400- to 500-year age classes exist. What's more, there are large Douglas-firs about 700 years old in the Ohanapecosh Valley—very rare—but indicating the possibility of a third fire reflected within the living age-structure of that beleaguered valley forest! By now, it must be admitted, we're pushing evidence to the limit. The combination of natural old-age mortality and fire-induced mortality from more than two holocausts has so depleted the ancient, original forest that the statistics from any local area cannot be trusted. Multiple disturbances so long ago are difficult to resolve from sparse records of old-growth survivors.

We walk down Laughingwater Creek Trail on the way back. Looking around at the big trees, we think about forests born in the wake of scorching devastation. And yet—can our impressions of lush greenery and wetness be so illusive? The knees of our trousers are still wet from contact with saturated logs and litter while searching for charcoal. In these wet, snowy climates, could the forest fuels really dry out? What kind of conditions gave rise to the great holocausts?

The Pacific Northwest can have long, dry summers. The summer of 1933 was particularly dry—and the Tillamook fire raged out of control. Scientists know from their studies of tree rings that episodes of drought have occurred in prehistoric times in the Northwest; old trees with narrow tree ring widths are associated with dry years. Sometimes winter precipitation cannot compensate for the previous summer's evaporation. Or perhaps dry summers and dry winters follow on the heels of one another. Put another way, those logs on the forest floor are drying out after several years of below average precipitation. Forests can approach ignition dryness especially when tree ring records reveal periods of drought lasting up to six

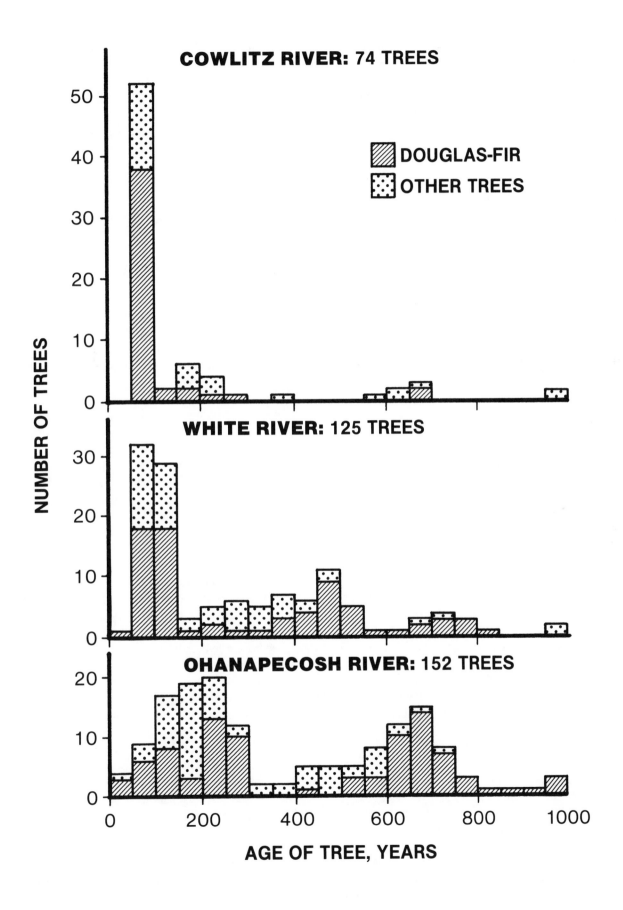

Figure 22. Sample age distribution of oldest trees in three river drainages.

52

years or more.

Regardless of the duration or intensity of drought, there's another factor at work. Once started, a fire releases great amounts of heat. Suppose a large forest region is near the verge of tinder dryness after some years of a climatic dry spell. Certain fuels may not be quite ready for ignition, while others, perhaps finer twigs, branches, or whatever, are powder kegs. A fire, well underway, can generate enough heat to dry beyond kindling temperature those other fuels that were somewhat more moist. In addition, the temperatures at the fire front are very high. The bulk of the fuel complex has now become a powder keg and — whoosh!—the holocaust is powered by the momentum of its own heat.

Just how dry a fuel must be to ignite is a complex subject. The green canopies of subalpine fir contain enough resins to be veritable torches upon the slightest drying. Stands near Grand Park were good examples of flammability when they were ignited by lightning a few years ago. Logs, on the other hand, might take many, many years of drying before they could carry a fire. Our impressions of dampness and verdure here are not so misleading. These stands along the Laughingwater might thrive for centuries before any drought reaches the intensity to dry them to the degree that they can support a fire. We continue along the path somewhat reassured.

On the basis of all this sleuthing, we can arrive at a fairly general picture of fire patterns and history in the park. Each of the major valleys around Mount Rainier is different. Figure 22 shows the age distribution (determined from increment cores and stump sections) of old trees in the Cowlitz, White, and Ohanapecosh drainages. The specimens of Douglas-fir, western white pine, noble fir, and other trees in the histograms were among the oldest individuals having an opportunity to invade disturbed areas. The most common disturbance agent was fire.

The pattern for the Ohanapecosh drainage, which includes the Laughingwater Creek and Silver Falls Loop trails, shows three modes of forest establishment. Peaks occur at 200 to 250, 650 to 700, and 900 to 1,000 years. Because seedling establishment can lag many years behind the fire, it is not unreasonable to speculate that important fire episodes took place sometime after about 250, 700, and 1,000 years ago. Other, more localized fire occurrences might be reflected by trees at age intervals between the major modes of Figure 22.

The Cowlitz drainage has been heavily burned the last two centuries. The histogram shows modes of forest establishment at 50 to 100, 150 to 200, and 650

to 700 years. The 50 to 100 peak doubtless reflects the many fires between 1886-1899 mentioned by Plummer. The "ancient burns" giving rise to the 650- to 700-year-old stands along Nickel Creek may or may not be contemporaneous with fires that produced the same age class in the Ohanapecosh drainage. The 1000-year class is represented by a forest stand near the headwaters of Williwaukas Creek. This stand of ancient Alaska yellow-cedar and mountain hemlock in a wet and sheltered valley has perhaps never seen a fire.

Still other age distributions are seen in the White Valley. The youngest mode (50 to 100 years) reveals fires related to white man's activities, especially the so-called "sheepherder burn" on Crystal Mountain. The early sheepherders burned forests along ridges and forest margins to provide more forage for their flocks, although few ever admitted to this practice...especially when a fire got out of hand and burned the whole valley side! Other major old-tree peaks in the White River drainage are at 450 to 500 years and 650 to 700 years. The former is not so apparent in the other drainages, suggesting that at least some of the fires centuries ago in the White River area never reached the Ohanapecosh and vice versa. The fog-drippy or snowpacked forests at Cayuse Pass presented an effective fire barrier. But the peak at 650-700 years overlaps the old-tree modes in both the Ohanapecosh and Cowlitz areas, where we suggested a period of fire or fires after about 700 years. More tantalizing is the fact that old trees in a 700 to 750 age distribution are widely scattered throughout the entire park. Could these old trees be the remnants of some super-holocaust or series of holocausts during an especially severe drought cycle? Could it be that a unique reality might have been witnessed by extant Indian tribes—not of the volcano smoking, but a huge billowing circle of smoke all around it? Maybe our imagination has carried us beyond the threshold of fact, but those 700-year-old trees are found almost everywhere nonetheless.

When Fred Plummer visited the Nisqually Valley in the summers of 1898 and 1899, he found 39,000 acres that were "timbered" including areas outside the park. These were essentially well-stocked stands of the larger-sized trees. Such stands are encountered along the park drive from the entrance to Longmire and from there along the road to Paradise. If one looks carefully, some of the massive Douglas-firs will be seen to have fire-scarred trunks. Many of these forests, too, are two-aged from multiple fires or fire episodes separated by centuries. Plummer found 28,000 acres to be "burned"—usually partially to fully

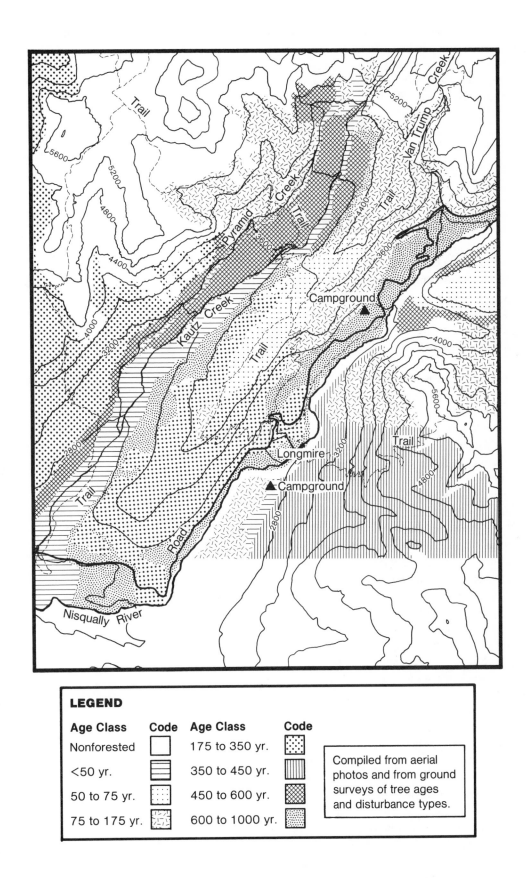

Figure 23. Forest age patterns, Rampart Ridge. (Map by permission of Miles Hemstrom.)

54

stocked sapling or pole stands. A typical burned forest occurs over much of Rampart Ridge. Actually not a single fire, but a complex of fires, many probably lightning-caused, swept this ridge.

Intricate patterns of young and old forests in the vicinity of Rampart Ridge are shown in Figure 23. Of special interest are remnants of old-growth forests along the wetter valley and lower slopes subtending Rampart Ridge. These stands escaped the many fires of recent years. A population of Douglas-firs at Cougar Rocks campground has avoided destruction for over a thousand years. Why? That population is mostly contiguous with other, younger forests all around, but has somehow led a charmed life. We can only speculate. Maybe this stand was isolated on a river bar when ancient fires raged up the Nisqually Valley. Maybe when the antics of Enumclaw and Kokoonis, those playful, mischievous spirits of thunder and lightning, were causing storms to pass over the ridge, the big flashes ignited only stands on the ridgetops or mid to upper slopes. The updrafts created by the heat of fires tend to propel them upslope, and away from the old growth below. Or possibly the fuel moisture in those groves of wetter habitats was just too high to carry a really hot fire needed to kill the trees. Or what about just blind luck?

Other valleys around Mount Rainier have their distinctive fire histories and forest patterns. The giant trees of the Carbon River Valley are in an age-class centered around 550 years. Even that wet valley burned! The high forests of Sunset Park burned extensively at some undetermined date. Skeletons of subalpine fir cover hundreds of acres, and forest reestablishment is taking place only very slowly. At still other high forest locations even-aged stands of noble fir can be discovered, accompanied by the usual charcoal evidence of fire. A 300- to 350-year-old grove of noble fir can be seen, for example, near the summit of Gobblers Knob; a similar age class occurs between Nahunta Falls and the Nisqually River bridge.

Much of the forest diversity enjoyed at Mount Rainier is the result of the many past fires. In the next chapter we will see how forest patterns are brought about by fire as we examine examples of fire succession. Were it not for these old and recent burns, the forests over much of the landscape would be rather monotonous—and probably composed mostly of western hemlock and silver fir. To be sure, other disturbances —floods, avalanches, volcanic eruptions, mudflows, landslides, windthrow, insect outbreaks— also initiate forest diversity. But fire is the most extensive and ubiquitous shaper of forest patterns, and for this reason we must appreciate the contribution of catastrophic fire to the richness of forests here.

We salute those hidden pieces of charcoal on the forest floor.

Chapter 5
Fire Succession

The land appears bleak and friendless. A fire holocaust has transformed the tall forest into a dismal graveyard of charred and dying skeletons. Here and there are smoldering logs where recent rains failed to quench lingering embers. Everywhere are ashes, blackened stems, and leaves not directly scorched but turning brown because the stems were sizzled by heat.

Appearances are deceiving. If beauty is only skin deep, so is the death of a forest after fire. In reality, the earth has just had a massage. Rains once held back in part by tall canopies have now fully soaked the soil. The mantle of fertilizing ashes provides a rich, sweet balm of minerals. Warm sunshine heats the soil to temperatures that evoke dormant responses after long centuries of cool shade. It's a gardener's delight, these moist, fertile, warm, sun-drenched soils—and the response is almost instantaneous. Even as lazy smoke curls and wisps into invisibility, another kind of invisibility is stirring

below the ashes and embers. For the soil is very much alive, not just with seeds, but with many kinds of plants whose below-ground parts did not perish in the fire. Now, with the suppressive effects of the tree layer removed, a new plant life is ready to begin.

Let us think of succession as a predictable sequence in time of plant communities on any particular land area. In this chapter we will examine some examples of the gradual and continuous, predictable process by which plants repopulate the burned forest. The subject is complex and, at Mount Rainier, not yet very well known. Since we cannot stand on a particular parcel of burned-over land for a thousand years to witness the sequence of plant communities, we will have to draw careful inferences by visiting forest landscapes that have burned in the past. Each of the forest types of Chapter 2 (the old forests of Table 1) has a different pattern of fire succession, because the environments of each are different. Let us then draw examples of the sequence of plant communities that follow fire from among those forest types whose fire-derived communities are especially conspicuous in the park.

TYPICAL SUCCESSIONAL PATTERN IN *ABIES AMABILIS* ZONE

125 years

250 years

500 years

750 years

Figure 24. Generalized stages of forest succession after fire at low and intermediate elevations, Mount Rainier National Park. The example shown above is for Pacific silver fir (Abies amabilis).

Fire in the SILVER FIR/OREGON GRAPE Environment

The fires of the SILVER FIR/OREGON GRAPE forests are often hot and intense. The fires travel along the ground and through tree crowns, leaving large openings and a few tree survivors. Such were the fires at Shriner Peak, which occurred in 1929 and again in 1934.

The forest environment along the lower-elevation segment of the Shriner Peak Trail is one of the warmest and driest in the entire park. The numerous openings here allow us to see the kinds of plant communities that follow the early years after fire. One of the most conspicuous plants is bracken fern, which is found in hot, sunny openings. It is doubtless an invader into newly-created openings, since its spores are readily carried by wind. Once established, bracken fern is tenacious, spreading by underground stems and soon controlling the site. On hot, dry slopes such as these the fern may persist for 125 years or more, well into later successional communities. On somewhat

56

Figure 25. Bracken fern is a common plant in early stages of fire succession. This stand of pole Douglas-firs occurs on the slopes of Backbone Ridge. The meter stick is near a charred snag, a remnant of the forest destroyed by fire sometime around 1890.

wetter sites it may not persist so long, although there are examples of bracken fern lasting in the understory of established forests up to 250 years in age. It is possible, therefore, that the fern might have occurred here and there in the pre-burn forest along the Shriner Peak Trail, and rapidly spread into the fire-created openings.

Older common herbs include two kinds of strawberry, lupine, Ross and Geyer sedges, white-flowered hawkweed, wild blackberry, and starflower. Some of these are "residual" plants that survive fire and then spread rapidly by seed or vegetative propagation. Others are "invaders" or pioneering plants that persist only as long as the openings. The common shrubs, such as sticky laurel, vine maple, and bearberry, include both types of plants.

The contrasting ecology of sticky laurel,

bearberry, and vine maple makes them strange bedfellows. Sticky laurel (sometimes known as snowbrush) commonly invades burns and burned clearcuts in the Pacific Northwest and northern Rocky Mountains. Its seeds lie dormant for decades or even centuries following the disappearance of the last mature plant. The heat of the fire cracks the previously impervious seedcoats and allows the seeds to absorb water and germinate. The plants grow rapidly in the hot, sunny openings. Sticky laurel has roots with nodules containing bacteria capable of taking nitrogen from the atmosphere and putting it into chemical forms useful to the sticky laurel and other plants. The thick, sticky, evergreen leaves are adapted to long growing seasons and droughty sites, a subject that is discussed later in this chapter. This shrub also is responsible for the distinctive, sweet aroma encountered on these dry sites on warm days.

The prostrate bearberry or kinnikinnick spreads vigorously over the dry soils of the hot openings. Like its taller cousins, the manzanitas, bearberry can easily withstand the heat and dessication. Indeed, severe sites, including the open forests of recent mudflow surfaces (for example, near the old Longmire Campground) and rocky sideslopes, are habitat for this attractive evergreen species. The bearberry arrived here at Shriner via the intestine of some animal, for as its name implies, the berries are sought by bears as food and the seeds pass unharmed through the gut ready to germinate upon opportunity. The plants here will persist so long as rather open conditions are present.

Vine maple is a most resourceful plant. It can take advantage of burns or openings as either a residual or invader species. In the former case, it reproduces by sprouting and, in the latter, by seeds blown in from other areas. Thus vine maple thickets are quickly formed, most often in draws or other well-watered areas. Scouler's willow and wild cherry are commonly associated with the maple thickets. They gradually die out as the forest returns. But the vine maple persists. As an understory shrub, it can revert to yet a third mode of reproduction—rooting. This takes place when branches come into contact with, or are buried in, soil. Is it any wonder that vine maple is one of the most common shrubs of the low and intermediate elevation forests?

We can refer to the openings dominated by ferns and other herbs or by a variety of shrubs as the herb-shrub stage of succession. As a rule, trees are absent or at best represented by only a few infrequent individuals. Elsewhere in the area, however, we find places where trees ranging in age from a few to about 60 years old are gradually filling in the openings. This early regenerative phase of succession by tree invaders can be described as a seedling-sapling stage. Seedlings are very young trees, often around ankle height, that have just survived the rigors of germination and early establishment; saplings are young trees with stems from mere whips to about 10 or 12 inches in diameter.

The trees of the seedling-sapling stage along the Shriner Peak Trail are almost all Douglas-fir. A few western white pine and noble fir also can be found. These young trees of the openings have canopies flooded by light on all sides and grow vigorously. Sooner or later, the openings become filled by more trees or by existing tree growth; the growing trees then experience both shading and root competition from neighboring trees. Further invasion

by any of the previously mentioned tree species ceases, for these trees are light-demanding and incapable of germinating and surviving under their own dense shade.

The next stage of forest succession is dominated by the rapidly growing Douglas-fir. We can envision a dense stand of tall stems that elevate a green canopy layer ever higher and leave behind a wake of dead branches and smaller trees that became too shaded. As the stand thins itself by tree-to-tree competition (not just for light but for limited soil nutrients, too), the surviving trees continue to grow; their stems are mostly in the range of 10-20 inches diameter at breast height. These sizes of trees are sometimes known as poles; they identify the pole stage of succession. Another feature of this stage is the scattering of small western hemlock seedlings or saplings in the shade of the Douglas-fir canopy. Although western hemlock also grows well in lighted openings, it is rare because of the hot, dry conditions there. But it can also germinate and grow in shaded areas, when environmental conditions at ground level are no longer so hot as in the herb-shrub openings.

Some additional plants gradually appear under the shaded conditions on these comparatively dry slopes: twinflower, pipsissewa, Oregon grape. But others are dying out or are already gone, including the light-demanding and heat-tolerant shrubs of sticky laurel and bearberry. Even such stalwarts as bracken fern find shade and soil conditions in the dense pole stand quite limiting, and there is a noticeable thinning in the density of fronds compared to sunny sites.

So far we've described three stages of fire succession. But we have said nothing about how long each lasts before progressing to the next. The duration of these stages is highly variable. Along the Shriner Peak Trail, for example, we have seen many areas still in the herb-shrub stage some 50 years after the fire, while other places in the same burn area are clearly in the seedling-sapling stage of reforestation. This emphasizes the fact that it can be many years, even decades, after a fire event before trees again become established; the exact time is influenced by several overlapping factors, including good tree seed supplies, favorable ground-level microclimates for germination and survival, and the degree of competition from the herbs and shrubs.

Often the oldest trees of a stand are used to approximate the date of the fire, especially with species such as Douglas-fir or western white pine, which need well-lighted clearings for establishment and can be assumed to be among the first wave of tree invasion at the onset of the seedling-sapling stage.

However, it should now be clear that the oldest trees do not give the date of the fire; the difference represents the approximate duration of the herb-shrub stage. How long the seedling-sapling stage lasts also varies, because the openings do not fill in all at once but over a period of years—perhaps 50 years or more on hot, dry slopes such as these. On the other hand, locally favorable microsites might quickly fill with trees and attain pole stage in a matter of decades. Examples are the pole stands along the initial portions of the Shriner Peak Trail. These stands are growing on lower slopes, where more favorable moisture conditions are a likely cause of the more rapid reforestation.

The pole stage lasts until the oldest trees are somewhere around 200 years old, and then gradually progresses to a mature forest stage. Western hemlock, which began as scattered seedlings in the early pole stage, becomes a more aggressive invader and will continue to maintain a rather constant supply of new tree regeneration through the remaining succession. Western redcedar, another shade-tolerant tree, also can

be found as regeneration in pole and mature forest stages, but is not as common as the hemlock. Mature forests are indicated by larger tree stem sizes (mostly over 20 inches) of the dominant trees and the gradual opening of the canopy as mortality takes its toll among taller trees. Down logs of larger-sized stems appear on the forest floor, while the proportion of Douglas-fir in the tall canopy gradually declines, with replacement by western hemlock and occasional western redcedar. After about 500 years (as measured by the oldest trees in the stand), 50 percent or so of the overstory will consist of western hemlock.

Several other features characterize the mature forest stage. Among the young tree regeneration appears silver fir, which gradually increases in abundance until its ratio to western hemlock regeneration is about 2:1. The hemlock seedlings are more and more likely to be rooted upon old logs, while silver fir can be just about anywhere. Silver fir is considerably more shade-tolerant than either hemlock or western redcedar, and will therefore persist in this stage and the forests to

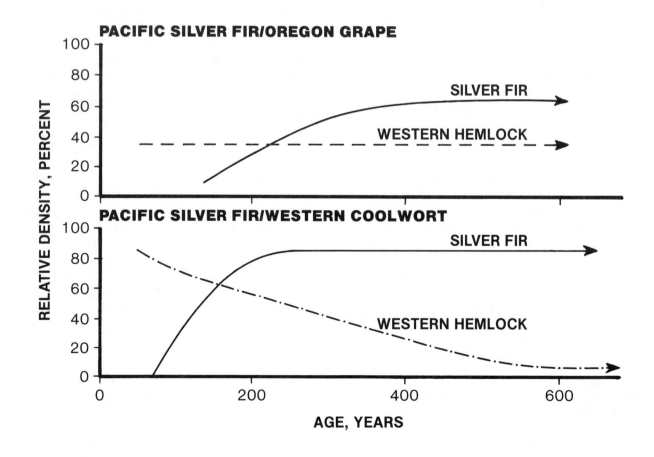

Figure 26. Fire chronosequences in silver fir/Oregon grape and silver fir/western coolwort (foamflower) forest types.

follow. But it grows rather slowly in the forest interior, especially in stands found on dry, south- or west-facing midslopes. After about five or six centuries silver fir may attain pole sizes here and there; a few might even reach the tallest canopy level. But generally, the mature forest is still dominated by Douglas-fir and western hemlock.

Except for vine maple, the herbs and shrubs of earlier stages have disappeared. We have noted how mortality was intense during the pole stage; few survived much into the early mature forest, and only the stubborn bracken fern remains there. Actually, even the mature forest stage has a sparse understory flora. The most continuous greenery is furnished by mosses, supplemented by a somewhat erratic population of Oregon grape, pipsissewa, twinflower, wintergreen, a few other evergreen plants, and a scattering of black and red huckleberry, vanilla leaf, and sword fern. But unlike many other forest types at Mount Rainier,

this stage of the SILVER FIR/OREGON GRAPE environment can hardly be said to have a dense or lush understory.

Because the fires at Shriner Peak were so recent, we cannot find mature stages of forest succession along the trail here. Instead, we must rely for our information on older forests at nearby locations, growing on similar soils, slopes, and exposures. Such forests are found at Deer Creek as well as the west-facing slopes of our traverse in Chapter 2. We must also assume that the ancient fires that gave rise to these mature forests created conditions not unlike the hot, dry conditions of the Shriner Peak Trail today. Only by making these assumptions and carefully selecting forest examples from various locations can we put together a time sequence of forest stands that spans all the successional stages.

When does succession end? The answer, quite simply, is when no further changes in the

Figure 27. Mature forest of the silver fir/Oregon grape forest type about 400 to 500 years after fire.

proportions of the major plant species of an area are taking place. Understory shrubs and herbs generally achieve more or less stable population levels during the mature forest stage; it takes longer for trees. Douglas-firs will persist for centuries after effective regeneration has ceased. One of the best ways to tell whether succession continues is to compare the composition of trees in the overstory with the composition of their replacement stock in the advancing regeneration beneath. A 600-year-old mature forest stand of the SILVER FIR/OREGON GRAPE type is likely to have an overstory mix of western hemlock and Douglas-fir and understory saplings and poles of mixed silver fir and western hemlock. This discrepancy lets us know that succession is continuing, so far as trees are concerned. But sooner or later, in theory, the ratios of tree dominants and their replacements will become fixed. These are equilibrium forests, or climaxes, and are considered to terminate succession. We suspect that silver fir and western hemlock can assume canopy dominance in about a ratio of 2:1, whereas in regeneration another ratio might be necessary to maintain such canopy dominance in this SILVER FIR/OREGON GRAPE environment. When these ratios are attained, no further changes of significance will occur in tree composition, and succession terminates. We have never seen any such forest. It simply takes too long for this to happen on essentially hot, dry slopes. More likely, another disturbance will start the whole process of succession over again.

Fire in the SILVER FIR/ALASKA HUCKLEBERRY Environment

Frequent, extensive fires in Stevens Canyon and the Cowlitz Valley permit study of early forest succession in environments much different from the hot, dry slopes of Shriner Peak. Instead, we find well-watered lower slopes, benches, and valley bottoms. The Wonderland Trail from the Box Canyon of the Cowlitz into Stevens Canyon is a good place to see some of the stages. The fires that destroyed the previous forest occurred possibly as early as 1841 and again in 1856 and 1886. There may have been some reburns in the decade following 1886.

Today we find a profusion of herbs and shrubs in the fire-created openings. Between the charred snags are patches of vine maple and dense bracken fern. Joining these are red alder, red huckleberry, hazelnut, Oregon grape, evergreen violet, vanilla leaf, twinflower, bunchberry, and dwarf bramble. This vegetation is similar to the herb-shrub stage of our previous example, except we notice that the openings are smaller and the vegetation is far more luxuriant. In addition, this stage does not last very long; within a decade after a fire, many locations will become restocked with another generation of trees.

The seedling-sapling stage has both Douglas-fir and western hemlock as prominent species. Locally abundant may be western white pine, noble fir, and western redcedar. Tree growth is rapid, and competition for light among the young trees soon becomes severe. Douglas-fir, western white pine, and noble fir outpace the other species and within a few decades achieve canopy dominance as stands of young poles, with hemlock and western redcedar as understory saplings or more recent seedlings. In the understory of 60- to 100-year-old pole thickets, the shrubs and herbs may decline somewhat in abundance; but they do not seem to be as severely limited as they were in comparable thickets of the drier slopes along the Shriner Peak Trail.

These early stages of fire succession in the Cowlitz Valley below Box Canyon and adjoining locations are mostly represented by the DOUGLAS-FIR/EVERGREEN VIOLET forest type, mostly young stands under about 150 years old as measured by the oldest trees, interrupted by small openings. Fires were so frequent and recent here that older forests are not found. Therefore we move on to the nearby Ohanapecosh Valley, where similar sites at about the same elevation feature 200- to 250-year-old forests that represent advanced successional stages. But how do we know these older stands represent the continuation of succession described for the Cowlitz Valley and vicinity? We must base this conjecture on the following evidence:

1. The physical environments (elevation, lower slopes and valleys, well-watered soils) are similar at both places.

2. The understory vegetation in pole stages of forest along the Cowlitz is nearly identical to the understory in mature stages of forest along the Ohanapecosh. This suggests that the forest microenvironment is about the same at both places.

3. The tree structure of Ohanapecosh forests represents a continuation of growth and regeneration shown in the oldest forests of the Cowlitz area. For example, silver fir first appear as seedlings and later as saplings in the pole-sized forests of the Cowlitz Valley and are found more commonly as seedlings, saplings, and taller poles in the 200- to 250-year-old stands along the Ohanapecosh.

If these assumptions are reasonable, then we must suppose one final condition before continuing with the sequence of forest stages. We know that fires at both places wiped out the pre-existing tree populations nearly completely and produced large openings. Let's suppose that the catastrophes that gave rise to the Douglas-fir and western hemlock forests along the Ohanapecosh over two and one-half centuries ago created the same kind of post-fire "initial conditions" that the fires produced near the end of the 19th century in the Cowlitz. If climates were much different during the centuries that separated these fires, these differences were not strong enough to alter the probabilities as to which trees, shrubs, and herbs would become established in the new openings. In other words, each forest area began its succession under the same set of rules.

Turning therefore to forests in the nearby Ohanapecosh Valley, we find the next stage of fire succession following 100- to 150-year-old pole stands in the Cowlitz to be represented by 200- to 250-year-old stands of the SILVER FIR/ALASKA HUCKLE-BERRY forest type. We can see this type of forest in the vicinity of Silver Falls. Look for an understory dominated by Alaska and red huckleberry, Oregon grape, twinflower, evergreen violet, vanilla leaf, and pipsissewa. Carpets of mosses are extensive. Don't expect any bracken fern; its day is over. So too for red alder. Both are early succession species and seldom last beyond the pole stage. The understory of this 200- to 250-year-old stand appears to be a more luxuriant version of the one we described in the SILVER FIR/OREGON GRAPE forest. The greater abundance of shrubs and herbs reflects the wetter sites of these lower slopes or benches.

The tree structure suggests that succession has progressed into a young phase of the mature forest stage. The tree canopy is 220-240 feet tall and rather open. Some of the larger trees are two or three feet in diameter; these are western hemlock and Douglas-fir. Pole-sized specimens not quite so tall include plenty of western hemlock and fewer western redcedar and Douglas-fir. The latter is probably of the same generation as the overstory Douglas-fir but became overtopped and suppressed by its faster-growing neighbors. At still lower tree levels are saplings, mostly of western hemlock but also western redcedar and a few silver fir. Seedlings of western hemlock are also abundant, especially on raised seedbeds such as punky logs and root mounds. It is clear that hemlock will maintain itself within this forest for centuries, since all sizes and ages of regeneration and advanced growth are common. Silver fir and western redcedar are less common as seedlings, but their shade tolerance assures them continuance as forests get older.

Still older forests of our after-fire sequence can be seen along the Olallie Creek-Cowlitz Divide Trail on broad, flat benches around 2500-2600 feet elevation. A check for charcoal in the soil confirms that these stands, now about 700 years old, originated by fire. The surviving Douglas-firs and western hemlocks of the overstory, and some western redcedars, now are massive trees, impressive to behold. But the most apparent difference in tree structure from the younger stands near Silver Falls is the abundance of both young and advanced regeneration by silver fir. Few trees have yet reached the tallest canopy level, but many have diameters around 20 inches and are over 150 feet tall. At sapling sizes, both silver fir and western hemlock seem about equally common, and we have no difficulty finding a profusion of seedlings of both species as we peer among the foliage of shrubs and herbs for ankle-height young trees. If we apply the "comparative ratios" test to the tree composition of the overstory and to the advancing regeneration beneath, we conclude that this 700-year-old forest is not a climax. There are too many silver firs in regeneration and not enough among the dominant overstory populations. But we can surmise that the climax forest would consist mostly of silver fir and a smaller amount of western hemlock. Western redcedar would probably be rare, and Douglas-fir, noble fir, and western white pine all absent. Considering the natural longevity of some of these species, however, many centuries will elapse before such a population will develop.

The SILVER FIR/ALASKA HUCKLEBERRY forest type is extensive at Mount Rainier, and we mentioned in Chapter 1 that numerous variations occur. Therefore, we do not expect fire sequences everywhere to be exactly as described in our example. Indeed, this example was drawn from the OREGON GRAPE PHASE of the type, a phase that represents a warmer and drier environmental variation of the lower elevations. However, considerably more research by forest ecologists will be needed before the other patterns of fire succession within the SILVER FIR/ALASKA HUCKLEBERRY environment can be understood.

Fire in SILVER FIR/SALAL Environment

One of the most fascinating examples of fire succession is found on the hot, dry upper slopes and ridgetops of intermediate elevations (3300-4300 feet). An unusual feature here is that just about the same understory vegetation is found in all the stages. But doesn't this violate the concept of succession, which we defined as a sequence of plant communities in any

62

given area? Let's follow through time the aftermath of a fire, and see what goes on here.

The fire succession pattern on SILVER FIR/ SALAL habitat can be seen in early stages at many park locations, including Rampart Ridge, Paul Peak Trail, the Wonderland Trail along hot slopes of the Puyallup Valley, and Klapatche Ridge. Some of these burns occurred over a hundred years ago and others more recently, but one thing these places share in common is thickets of salal, sometimes in large openings, sometimes under trees. Quite possibly a very short (one to two year) period of herb dominance immediately followed the fire. One of the conspicuous herbs would be fireweed, a common seed invader of new forest clearings in this region. But the fireweed stage would be very brief, since residual shrubs quickly "rebound" after fire.

Heat penetration from a fire into the soil is governed by temperatures at the surface, soil texture, humus content, soil moisture and other factors, but the heat rapidly attenuates with depth because mineral soil is a good insulator. Conduction of heat into moist soils is slower, since some of the heat energy is dissipated by the vaporization of water. Temperature sensors as little as a quarter of an inch below ground may show little or no rise in temperature as the fire front passes, particularly if the fire is a fast-burning "flash" fire whose transient high temperatures are very brief. Fires that persist around logs or wood piles can cause high temperatures up to five inches below the soil surface, but beyond this depth the heat is rarely lethal. Certain kinds of fire, such as crown fires, consume fuels and release their greatest heat energy at various heights above the ground surface.

In some cases these fires cause little harm to plant stems or buds at or near ground level, although shoots at levels of greater heat release may be killed. Therefore, after the fire has passed there can exist from about ground level or slightly above, even to shallow depths within the soil, an envelope of plant tissues that were generally unaffected by the fire.

Within a few years at most, the openings created by fire are again dominated by salal and its associated shrubs: beargrass, red huckleberry, Oregon grape, pipsissewa. Vine maple may be present, but on these hot upper slopes it is usually minor and infre- quent. But the others, especially salal and beargrass, form a dense, continuous cover among the blackened snags and fallen logs of the clearings. There are no trees of any size. The beneficial warmth and sunshine of the clearings, and possibly the elimination of water and nutrient competition from trees, cause salal and other shrubs to spread and dominate. This happens so

quickly that within a few years the blackened logs are masked by rich sheets of green foliage. The salal- beargrass explosion serves to retain mineral nutrients as a part of the living biomass, rather than allow their loss through leaching and soil erosion. One effect of fire has been to transfer mineral nutrients from tree to shrub biomass.

The dominant plants of these clearings have numerous adaptations that make them so successful on the hot, dry slopes. Salal has broad, evergreen leaves with thick, waxy coatings, well displayed at regular intervals along elongate, arching branches. The whole architecture of the shoot bespeaks efficient light capture and minimization of water loss from leaf surfaces. Below ground, salal has a maze of creeping horizontal rhizomes, useful both for food storage and exploring new ground. After a shoot-killing fire, the dormant buds along the rhizome are quickly activated into growth. By mobilizing the food reserves of the underground stem, the buds soon grow to the ground surface as new branches where, under the stimulus of sunlight, new leaves are formed.

Beargrass has thick, evergreen leaves, narrow and grass-like, displayed in a rosette-like pattern. Such a geometry allows the plant to capture light effectively, regulate leaf temperaturs, and reduce water losses during the hot summer months. Just below ground level is a thick root crown for food storage; from this a massive root system spreads in all directions. Beargrass is almost unbelievable in its ability to survive fire. The leaves can burn away, but insulated growing points near the center of the rosette survive and begin expanding almost as soon as the flames have passed.

Oregon grape has thick, evergreen, holly-like leaves, a fleshy root crown, and a well-developed, perennial root system. Pipsissewa grows with a dense rosette display of thick, evergreen leaves close to the ground. Its stem, like that of salal, is rhizomatous, and the roots are enveloped with fungus tissues in a symbiotic arrangement of nutrient absorption.

These adaptations answer a severe environ- ment in which light competition, food storage below ground, water conservation, and nutrient uptake are all survival factors. Year-round photosynthesis, courtesy of evergreen leaves, is an obvious advantage on warm slopes where snowpack levels are not great. But water losses from the hot, dry summer months, when humidity is low and rains are infrequent, must be kept to a minimum and leaves in full sunlight must not overheat; thus the narrow, thick leaf structure. Under- ground food storage organs provide multiple advan- tages. They tide evergreen plants through adverse

Figure 28. Beargrass resprouting one month after a fire.

seasons and confer a head start for exploiting open spaces after a fire. The extensive root systems can take full advantage of local water and nutrients.

And so salal, beargrass, and other associated plants of the shrub thickets command and exploit fully the limited growth resources of the hot, dry sites. If water, nutrients, and sunlight are so nicely apportioned among the shrubs (and a few herbs), how is it possible for other species, particularly the trees, to invade? In fact, very few trees can "beat the odds" in the shrubby clearings of this habitat. Many, many years can pass without a tree's appearing. The reign of salal and its associates sometimes seems almost absolute.

Trees able to break the ironclad grip of salal-beargrass thickets include Douglas-fir, western hemlock, western white pine, and noble fir. Once a seedling has reached the height of the upper shrub canopy, its probability for survival is good. But first the tree has to make it that far, and the odds against it

are staggering. It may take many years, numerous seed influxes, and some especially favorable sequences of above-average summer rains before any seedlings will survive. Newly germinated trees are heavily shaded at ground level. In July and August the water in the upper soil has been depleted by the shrubs. Soil mineral nutrients are quickly taken up by the vigorous salal, beargrass, or Oregon grape. The tree seedling is starved, smothered, and choked on all fronts. But trees are nothing if not persistent. Every few years, another seed crop "samples" the environment for an opportunity to grow. Another year brings a somewhat different growing season climate. Accidents of disease, insects, browsing, trampling, or whatever afflict a certain number of the shrubs or herbs. And at last the trees make it.

It is conceivable that a massive wave of new seedlings heralds the advent of the next forest. But more probable in these hot, shrub-controlled openings is the gradual process of tree invasion requiring decades. And so the new forest has humble beginnings with the emergence of a few scattered trees at and above the canopy level of salal and beargrass. Douglas-fir and western hemlock are the most likely trees to occur, for their seed sources are abundant in forests that adjoin the clearings. But western white pine and noble fir can also be among the early arrivals. During those years of reforestation—a stage that can be called seedling-sapling by analogy with our other examples of fire succession—we find low to moderate densities of tree stocking and a range of tree ages that might span a century.

Since the pressures for regeneration are more or less continuous, the openings gradually fill in with mixtures of western hemlock, Douglas-fir, western white pine, and noble fir. The pine and noble fir are not very common, and western redcedar is sometimes less frequent. Growth rates of these trees are poor on sites of the SILVER FIR/SALAL habitat. Because of the gradual invasion and slow growth, it may take a century or more before the forests close up the openings. That is why we can still see salal-dominated brushlands with scattered trees long after the fire itself has been forgotten. (Those trees, of course, are post-fire arrivals as indicated by their size and age. It is also possible to find now and then a larger, older pre-fire survivor within some openings, doubtless where crown fires were not carried and the transient heat of shrub-level flames did not penetrate the bark.)

The next stage of succession is represented by stands of pole-sized trees; their composition reflects the proportions of tree species that maintained height superiority throughout the seedling-sapling stage. But since their growth rates are slow, the tree heights at pole stage are not impressive, perhaps 80 to 100 feet. The most striking feature of the pole-sized stands is the continued strong dominance of the salal-beargrass assemblage despite shading by canopies of western hemlock and other trees. A pole stand of 140 years of age at Rampart Ridge, for example, has a ground cover of beargrass (30 percent of the area), salal (15 percent), Oregon grape (4 percent), pipsissewa (4 percent), and other species (about 10 percent). Although there may be some reduction in flower and fruit production, the shrubs seem to thrive almost as exuberantly as they do in the sunny openings. These stubborn plants refuse to be cowed by the trees that finally beat them for command of the sunlight.

The pole stands are almost perfectly two-tiered: a hemlock and Douglas-fir canopy above and a shrub canopy below. A low density but nevertheless rather constant supply of tree seedlings is hidden in the shrubs—mixtures of western hemlock, western redcedar, and now silver fir. But there are almost no lower-level trees of sapling size, or at least only a few—the occasional western hemlock or western redcedar— but the extreme sparseness of saplings hints that even now young trees have difficulty surviving among the shrubs...even the tough silver fir.

We have visited pole-sized western hemlock stands along the Paul Peak Trail, whose ages are around 300 years, and found fewer than two or three silver fir saplings per acre despite the fair quantity of seedlings in the area. The paucity of understory tree regeneration is understandable, for the struggling populations are now at a double disadvantage. The dense shrubs are still exerting strong ground level competition, and this is compounded by the additional light, nutrient, and water demands of the established crop of overstory trees. Perhaps one tree generation managed to beat the odds, but another generation apparently cannot, at least not in the pole stage. There simply isn't the abundance of resources to support more trees here.

We have not found successional stages older than about 300 years in this habitat. A 700-year-old stand of SILVER FIR/SALAL type can be found at about 3,000 feet elevation along the Eagle Peak Trail, but it occupies lower and middle slopes. This forest also witnessed a second fire about three or four centuries ago, as revealed by local inclusions of 300-year-old Dougas-firs among much older trees. Thus this later fire appears to have had a rather spotty burning behavior in contrast to the holocausts we depicted on drier upper slopes and ridges. Neverthe-less, this forest along the Eagle Peak Trail shows many characteristics of the mature forest stage of the SILVER FIR/SALAL environment. A salal-beargrass association covers about 30 percent of the forest floor, with some variation in cover and composition from one place to another. Alaska huckleberry constitutes about 15 percent of the ground cover, and red huckle-berry about 3 percent. It is not unusual to find red huckleberry more common than Alaska huckleberry on the dry upper slopes. Does this shift in their relative abundance in this stand reflect the well-watered site, or a change in the forest environments during the matura-tion of the forest? We don't know; either alternative, or both, is plausible.

There are ample quantities of seedlings here, mostly western hemlock, but many silver fir and western redcedar, too. Some of these are, by now, surviving into sapling and pole sizes. The space between the overstory tree and shrub-level canopies is beginning to fill with the greenery of advancing tree regeneration. But again we are cautioned to consider that this forest occupies rather well-watered mid and lower slopes.

How about those pole stands of the upper slopes and ridges—will their inner spaces be filling with saplings and poles after another four centuries of growth? The question may be academic, for stands much older than about 300 years are yet to be found along the hot, dry ridges and upper slopes. It seems that fires are just too frequent. For all their hard-fought victories, those pole-sized trees—like the ones they replaced—seem destined for a fiery death. Salal and beargrass have the adaptations to take these periodic fires in stride; the trees do not. Another tree crop will have to start all over again, and confront once more the implacable shrubs.

We can now suggest an answer to the question posed at the beginning: does succession really take place within this SILVER FIR/SALAL environment? Over the centuries there occurs a kind of rhythmic alternation between shrub dominance and tree dominance. The cadence of this rhythm is marked by the frequency of fire. This is a pendulum type of succession, where the ratio of trees to shrubs declines to zero, remains there awhile, gradually increases, and then drops to zero again (we might insert a stacatto point to represent the fireweed stage).

Since recurring fires bring about a kind of rhythmic stability to the vegetative expression, we can label as "fire climax" the pole forests of western hemlock and Douglas-fir with salal and beargrass beneath and silver fir seedlings that will never grow up. Perhaps this is a literal hell of a way to regulate the forests here—by scorching them periodically—but that's how it seems to be done. There's no question that life is tough in this habitat.

And those that endure it are tougher still.

Fire in the SILVER FIR/RUSTY LEAF Environment

The entire upper valley of Stevens Canyon is a disaster area. Just below Louise and Bench lakes the road traverses tall brushy thickets. As the road crosses Sunbeam and Stevens creeks we look down and across the canyon to a barren landscape of steep slopes, rubble chutes, tall cliffs streaked with water, avalanche tracks, and skeletons of trees. A pathetic forest is nothing more than an isolated tree or group of trees emerging above raggedy growths of shrubs. There is a sense of tension here, and few care to get out of the car or linger. The whole scene gives the uncomfortable

feeling that somehow one might get caught in an impending catastrophe. Let the ecologists hassle over those steep slopes and brush thickets; we're heading on to Box Canyon.

The fires that ravaged this area were continuations of "The Burn" that swept into the Cowlitz drainages in 1856 and 1886. Some clifftop forests and occasionally an older tree, perhaps buffered by boggy soil or rocky talus, escaped destruction. But when a tree appears above the extensive brushy areas, it is sometimes hard to decide if it survived the fire or came in later. One technique is to find the largest tree growing in close proximity to a heavily charred snag. A flame hot enough to brand a large tree is presumed to have killed smaller trees nearby. Thus, the living tree probably came in after the fire. Three or four trees selected in this manner at various brush-choked sites were all about 75-100 years old (in 1975), placing them after the time of the fire. Such trees, however, are few and far between. Some 90 to 120 years after the fires, this landscape of cold, wet elevations clearly belongs to the tall shrubs. Will forests ever come back?

I have found no description of the vegetation in those years immediately following fire. Today at Frog Heaven (which burned in 1894 as part of "Longmire's revenge" on the yellow jacket wasps), we can still find fireweed and bracken fern on somewhat drier sites. This suggests that at least in some places an herb-dominated stage might have followed fire in this SILVER FIR/RUSTY LEAF habitat. But if an herb stage did develop, it was neither very extensive nor long-persisting. At least there are no meadows today that compare to the bracken fern openings of lower elevations. At these cold, wet elevations the show after fire mostly belongs to the shrubs.

Sitka alder grows in the coastal lowlands, coast ranges, and taller mountains from Alaska to northern California—a geography influenced by moist Pacific air moving inland. Alder communities are found on sites under heavy winter snow accumulations and saturated soils in summer. The stems and branches are densely matted, and their growth forms make them just about impenetrable; indeed, they are the bane of cross-country hikers who learn after a single encounter to avoid the "green hell" at any cost. The limber stems are prostrate with the lower limbs directed downslope and the tips bowed upward and springing erect as soon as snows melt. Flexible stems and springy, bowed forms seem to be adaptations not to repulse hikers but to withstand snow creep and avalanches. (We can sometimes see a similar bowed base or "pistol butt" on tree saplings of steep, snow-

66

loaded slopes.) Pure thickets of Sitka alder often dominate steep slopes subject to recurrent snow avalanches, as well as burned forest areas where seepage waters flow.

The development of dense woody shrub stands in rapid response to fire is considered by many ecologists to be a mechanism to minimize loss of nutrients from the ecosystem. The regulation of nutrient cycling is achieved in several ways, of which one of the most important is these thickets with their "filtering" of nutrients in melt and runoff waters in the root zone and transpiration stream (the flow of water through stems and leaves that results in evaporative return of the water to the atmosphere). Nutrients in solution thus are retained in the shrubby biomass rather than lost from the slopes to the streams and rivers.

Another possible mechanism for retaining nutrients is the reduction of decomposition rates in the shaded thickets. In the absence of this shade the moist soils would be somewhat warmer (by sunshine), microbial activities of soil humus would be more rapid, and nutrients freed by organic breakdown would be leached into runoff waters. A third effect of the shrubs is to hold back the downslope movement of nutrients in the form of soil, i.e., to retard soil erosion. Foresters sometimes castigate the shrub stage of succession on disturbed slopes because, as we'll see, shrubs can retard rates of reforestation. But their important role in the retention of nutrients has become the subject of intensive research in recent years.

Sitka alder in profusion has another important nutrient cycling role in the burned landscape: the fixation of nitrogen. Bacteria at specialized root structures called nodules convert atmospheric nitrogen to forms available for utilization by the alder. When the leaves and roots of alder die and decompose, the organic nitrogen becomes available to other plants and microorganisms. On wet sites the populations of Sitka alder are probably the principal avenue whereby nitrogen is being "pumped" into the ecosystem.

Sitka alder is not the only tall shrub here at Stevens Canyon; we can also find rusty leaf (fool's or false huckleberry), rhododendron, oval-leaf huckleberry, and of shorter stature, black huckleberry. There may be some segregation of these species according to the degree of soil drainage and stage of reforestation, but the subject requires more study. However, one of the consistent and dominant shrubs of early reforestation (oldest trees about 75 to 100 years old) is rusty leaf, and because this shrub also maintains high cover in very old forest stands (Sitka alder does not), this habitat in forested expression has been called the SILVER FIR/RUSTY LEAF type.

High elevation brush thickets play ecological roles that have both similarities to and differences from the shrub thickets of lower elevations. The lower elevation salal-beargrass thickets are mainly evergreen, while the thickets of Sitka alder or rusty leaf are deciduous. This contrast of lifeform reflects adaptation to a markedly different environment at this elevation (about 4,400 feet just below Louise Lake).

There are short growing seasons and prolonged periods of plant dormancy under snowpack. Winter photosynthesis is impossible. Freezing temperatures are common even during the growing season, and minimum temperatures average much below those at lower elevations. The energy cost to sustain evergreen leaves all year outweighs the photosynthetic gains during the limited growing period. Shrubs therefore shed leaves when photosynthesis drops below critical levels for too long a time. But new leaves are produced almost as soon as the snow melts away from the shoot parts. Buds forsake dormancy when warmed by spring temperatures. Almost simultaneous processes of flowering and leafing produce an explosive, burgeoning event as the snows melt from the thickets. By the time the snowpack has fully melted, the leafing of most species has been completed, and very little of the precious photosynthetic opportunity has been lost.

Competition between trees and shrubs is intense. We can see for ourselves how long the brushy thickets continue to control most sites at upper Stevens Canyon and Frog Heaven. But many of these contain smaller trees within, and we can observe severe suppression of seedlings and saplings. A silver fir at waist height can be 100 years old. Measurements have also shown that, from a recruitment stock of about 19,000 individual tree seedlings, only about 300 will survive to pole or larger sizes. The competition isn't for water; there's a superabundance of that. It's light, nutrients, and heat that young trees crave. Heat? Recall that tree seedlings must contend with snowpack burial. The deeper the snow and the longer it takes to melt, the shorter the growing season for the emergent seedling. While shrubs of the brushy slopes can afford to shed leaves, the conifers cannot; they need every light beam they can trap. But virtually no light reaches them below snow. And when shaded by the expanded foliage of taller shrubs, the snow melts more slowly. Solar heat does good work on the shrub leaf surfaces, but that same heat is not melting snow. Small trees must wait another few days, and the growing season for them will be that much shorter. Some of the suppressed trees, unable to meet or replenish food reserves by means of photosynthesis, simply die. Heat also is needed for warming cold or frozen soils. Most conifers cannot grow well in cold soils, or worse, cold and saturated soils. The seedlings in those thickets are having a rough time.

Let's look now at some of the places where scattered trees or small groups of trees have emerged above the shrub canopies. Many are pole-sized trees that were early arrivals after the fire; their early growth had more or less kept up with the growing shrubs. A few might have been small trees at the time, spared by some fluke of fire-burning behavior. The principal early invaders and survivors among the emergent tall sapling and pole populations are silver fir, sub-alpine fir, and Alaska yellow-cedar. This rather remarkable assemblage is quite unlike the examples of succession from lower elevations. Foresters regard subalpine fir in the Cascade Range as an "intolerant" tree; it cannot germinate or grow well in shaded microsites. In the seedling-sapling stage at lower elevations we found Douglas-fir, western white pine, and noble fir to be intolerant trees of the comparable invasion stage of reforestation. Up here, however, these species and western hemlock comprise only about 25 percent of the early tree arrivals. Subalpine fir represents nearly 10 percent of the larger, emergent trees; perhaps many were established on sunny, warmer microsites where they managed to keep up with the growing shrubs. Alaska yellow-cedar, by contrast, is considered "tolerant"; it will germinate and grow in shade, and also is hardy and endurant in cold, wet soils. Silver fir is another tolerant species of the early invaders, and like subalpine fir, can grow well in sunny sites, too. Don't we recall that silver fir became important mostly in the mature and climax stages of fire succession in the other habitats? Indeed, at lower elevations. But in the cold, wet climates of the Mountain Hemlock Zone, the silver fir can also be one of the principal invaders of the earliest stage of reforestation. In fact, almost 70 percent of the seed-lings and saplings still hidden in the shrub thickets of these 75- to 100-year-old stands are silver firs. The remainder are subalpine fir, Alaska yellow-cedar, and occasional western and mountain hemlocks.

The numerous seedlings and small saplings within the thickets, and a scattering of emergent conifers, provide reassurance that the forests are coming back. Certainly the process is slow—in part because of shrub competition, in part because the climate for tree growth is rigorous. We may be impatient because we prefer forest vegetation to dreary shrub tangles. But no such value judgments hurry the natural process. To each its time and place, whether a matter of only a few years or a millenium.

If we really care to see old forests of the SILVER FIR/RUSTY LEAF type, we'll not linger in Stevens Canyon. The stands along Olallie and Kotsuck creeks are about 700 years old. The big trees are silver fir, Alaska yellow-cedar, and once in a while, mountain and western hemlocks. Subalpine firs are long gone. Somehow we appreciate these lovely stands all the more because we know something about their agonizing birth pains amid the alder and rusty leaf thickets. We may indeed have been uncomfort-able in Stevens Canyon; but as we hike up Olallie Creek, we become aware that this example of forest succession tells the story of rags to riches.

Fire in the SILVER FIR/BEARGRASS Environment

Among the most memorable experiences of the high country are the scenes and panoramas to be enjoyed from upper slopes, ridgetops, and the broad, flat expanses formed by Rainier's lava flows. Such views are obtained because of our elevated perspective in the upper parts of the landscape and because forests no longer close us in. These open spaces are formed from natural parks (Grand Park, Van Trump, Paradise, Moraine Park, and many others) and from other types of "meadows" that are not permanent, but instead are forests in early stages of fire succession. What's the difference, and how can we tell which is which? So far as vistas are concerned, there is no difference; the absence of closed forest allows views of glaciers and waterfalls, of Goat Rocks and other distant summits of the Cascades. But parks and burned forest clearings have very contrasting ecologies, for under present climates the forests will never claim the former, but sooner or later they will claim the latter. In other words, we can think of the parks as permanent open-ings and the burned forest clearings as temporary openings. But how do we know right now whether this opening, from which we gawk at the glacier-and-cloud drama high on the summit cone, is temporary or permanent?

Sunset Park is not a "park" at all, but a 3,500-acre burn that happened in November 1930 when a debris fire got away from a road crew. Weathered gray snags of subalpine fir and old downed logs remind us that this is forest land. Young trees here and there give evidence of succession. Grand Park has no such snags or logs, no hint in the least that trees ever were or will be there—a good example of a permanent, unforested opening or park. Sometimes a park can suddenly become invaded by trees, a phenomenon usually

68

associated with certain climatic changes that we will look at in Chapter 7. But more generally the parks remain treeless, even though there may be closed or open forest all around.

Another reliable measure of parks, in contrast with forest clearings, is the botanical composition. Plants of the permanent openings often are uncommon or absent in forested environments even when these have been opened up by fire. One of the most interesting examples is a small, yellow-flowered member of the carrot family, *Tauschia stricklandii*, known only from the parks of the northwest sector of Mount Rainier National Park. On the other hand, some plants of the forests are usually common in the burned openings, but not found in typical park environments. Two of the more important of these are beargrass and black huckleberry.

Visitors have no trouble identifying burned openings of the SILVER FIR/BEARGRASS forest type. Of course, the fire-tolerant beargrass is abundant, but another feature is that this is one of the best places to pick huckleberries in August and September. The black huckleberry shrubs yield prolific crops of berries most years in these sunny openings.

Certain herbs join ranks with the beargrass and black huckleberry after the fire. We'll see various high elevation grasses and sedges, lupines, valerian, woodrush, paintbrush, and others here and there. Many of these also grow in the plant communities of unforested parks. In the beargrass-black huckleberry openings, many high-light-demanding plants will decline as the forests return. Other plants here include forest-tolerant species such as trailing raspberry (*Rubus lasiococcus*), leafy lousewort, beadlily, and one-sided wintergreen. These are almost never found in parks. We can also mention some herbs conspicuous by their absence: twisted stalk, trillium and twayblade, which are particular to cool, shaded forest interiors; they are absent not because of fire-kill but because these openings are too hot and dry.

Trees come back to these burned clearings in patterns and slow rates rather similar to the salal-beargrass openings of the lower elevations. The reasons are probably much the same: competition from the established ground flora and rigorous climates. Nevertheless, beargrass is the harbinger of trees. On lower elevation sites—the WESTERN HEMLOCK phase of the type—just about any of the common conifers can be pioneers: western hemlock, Douglas-fir, subalpine fir, silver fir, noble fir, or Alaska yellow-cedar. But on many sites above about 4,500 feet in elevation—the MOUNTAIN HEMLOCK phase—the common pioneering species include subalpine fir,

silver fir, mountain hemlock, and Alaska yellow-cedar. As trees gradually return, we are again reminded of the park-like quality of the landscape, a pleasant arrangement of scattered trees, small groves, and a low, continuous cover of beargrass and huckleberry that guides our sight to the scenic features beyond. This reforestation, similar to the seedling-sapling stage of previous examples of succession, will continue until the openings are finally restocked and the foreground of our vistas closes with growing saplings.

Ecologists usually regard the SILVER FIR/BEARGRASS type as a comparatively dry, high elevation forest. But no land area is perfectly uniform. The variations in relief, snow accumulation and drainage patterns, and soil properties all influence where plant species are growing. Therefore we should not find it surprising to happen upon a thicket of rhododendron or rusty leaf (shrubs that prefer wet sites) in a predominantly beargrass meadow. Or consider Alaska yellow-cedar, a tree that requires very humid or rainy climates with substantial amounts of snowfall. It grows where the snowpack, slowly melting into early summer, produces cold, wet soils. At the other extreme is the subalpine fir of drier, well-drained, warm soils. It endures the same humid, snowy climates of this elevation, but finds these upper slope and ridge microenvironments congenial to its "warm-dry" requirements of germination and growth.

The composition of closed pole-sized stands can be as variable as the seedling-sapling stage which preceded. Along the trail to Spray Park, we can find a 200-year-old closed stand composed mostly of silver fir overstory as well as seedlings and saplings. There are minor quantities of subalpine fir in the overstory, and a minor representation of Alaska yellow-cedar and mountain hemlock in both overstory and regeneration. Not far from Three Lakes in the upper Panther Creek drainage, one of the burned upper slopes has all sizes and ages (up to about 165 years) of subalpine fir as the dominant tree, with minor densities of silver fir, western white pine, and mountain hemlock. And just before the Kautz Creek trail starts zig-zagging up steep slopes to Indian Henry's Hunting Ground, there is a pole stand of Douglas-firs with lesser amounts of western hemlock in the canopy overhead, and both western hemlock and silver fir well represented by regeneration. Despite this apparent diversity, the silver fir will be the principal tree to succeed eventually to canopy dominance. And need we be reminded that each of these stands has the signature of beargrass and black huckleberry?

The most advanced stage of succession is revealed by stands between 300 and 500 years old that

Figure 29. Subalpine fir and a few yellow-cedars are gradually filling in old burns at high elevation sites such as this ridgetop, which is comparatively warm and snow-free.

contain all sizes of silver fir. What a contrast from the SILVER FIR/SALAL type where stands are seldom over about 300 years old, and silver fir is still struggling to reach sapling size! In these older SILVER FIR/BEARGRASS stands, Alaska yellow-cedar is still represented by both young and advanced regeneration, but these are seldom as plentiful as comparable sizes of silver fir. Because variations in microrelief and soils are more or less unchanged throughout the stages of forest development, we can suggest that at least some of the cedars will always be around, perhaps on wetter or iron pan soils or on soils of poor oxygen

content here and there. Also, we always seem to find some mature western or mountain hemlock and a few saplings or small poles in the understory. An occasional specimen of light-demanding subalpine or noble fir in the overstory informs us that these stands originated in the seedling-sapling stage; but when they die, the silver fir or, less likely, hemlock or Alaska yellow-cedar will replace them.

A rather remarkable feature of succession is that many stands approaching the 500th year seem, by the comparative ratios test, to be realizing stable, climax condition. This has happened almost within a single tree generation, as measured by the longevity of the oldest subalpine or noble fir. At these high elevations—comparatively dry but watered through some of the summer by snowmelt—a forest once started seems almost to race to its climax. One explanation for this is that trees bring about shaded, cooler ground climates that prolong snowmelt and favor more rapid establishment and growth of silver fir. If water in the seedling root zone is more available, then competition for soil moisture with the beargrass-huckleberry assemblage is ameliorated and the tolerant silver fir (and occasional hemlock and Alaska yellow-cedar as well) enjoy accelerated regeneration success. This hypothesis would not apply to the SILVER FIR/SALAL type of the lower elevations, where the snow is not as deep and does not last as long because of the warmer climate.

Fires occur often enough, it seems, in the SILVER FIR/BEARGRASS environment to preclude finding many stands in the second generation of silver fir tree populations. But no matter; at least we can find first-generation stands of full silver fir regalia. And isn't the burned landscape's ability to heal itself as important as any temporary expression of vegetation? No ecologist or lay visitor can deny that the process of fire succession contributes a significant fourth dimension— time—to the forest landscape.

The narrow, pointed spires of subalpine fir, so distinctive along the road to Sunrise Ridge, are both beautiful and ephemeral. The tall, blue-crowned noble firs at Nahunta Falls will be gone within the century. The Douglas-firs of a thousand years at Cougar Rocks are on the way out. And these park-like openings among the beargrass will disappear.

But elsewhere the same kinds of forests are born again. As we have seen from a handful of examples, the ancient and recent fires have produced the patterns and diversity of most of today's forests. We cannot disparage those burned clearings, no matter how bleak or impenetrable or uncomfortably hot they may be. From struggles within the tangles of sapling thickets will emerge heroic specimens of trees a thousand years old.

Old growth is forever being created by fire. Fire, like climate and soil, or snow melting in late spring, or even a herd of elk passing through, is part of the forest environment, a factor of forest rhythms and regulation. It is also a part of forest evolution and coevolution. Why is the bark of old Douglas-firs so thick, and why are the seeds of sticky laurel stimulated by fire temperatures to germinate? Unless misused or misunderstood by man (which is why the study of fire ecology is important), fire—especially in the national parks—is not necessarily the "enemy" of forests, any more than are snow or browsing animals or volcanic eruptions. In the time scale of fire succession the fire event itself is to the forest but a flickering historic instant. It is the semicolon between phrases, the brief pause between inhalation and exhalation. We can see for ourselves that the forest landscapes along the flanks of this great volcano are enriched with trees and forest patterns—a quiltwork expression of the many past fires. The forests here are as continuous and enduring as the climates and soils that favor tree growth. Fires only make the forests more interesting.

Chapter 6
The Mudflow

"At the time of your death, my head will burst open. The water from the lake here will flow down my sides into the valleys below. I, Takobed, have spoken."

The old man died, and it was as he said. Takobed's head burst open, and the lake on top spilled out, and the water rushed down. It swept the trees from where Orting now is, and left the prairie covered with stones.
— Puyallup legend from *Indian Legends of the Pacific Northwest* by Ella E. Clark

The forests of the Tahoma Creek valley were doomed. Nearly 800 years of growth had produced stately stands of Douglas-fir, western hemlock, and western redcedar. Some of the Douglas-firs exceeded five feet in girth and were about 250 feet tall. The forest floor was richly carpeted by mosses, ferns, vine maple, and areas of Alaska huckleberry. Along the stream were groves of red alder growing on gravel bars and on the silts and sands behind beaver dams. But this placid scene was soon to end. For too many centuries, these forests had escaped the massive catastrophes that had repeatedly wiped out stretches of forests along other valleys. The forests below the Nisqually Glacier had been buried at least three times by surging mudflows. Those events, however, were nothing compared to the terrifying destruction a millenium earlier along the White River and its West Fork. The effects of that cataclysm were so profound that for generations most Northwest Indians avoided venturing onto the sacred, ice-laden slopes of Takhoma.[1]

The Osceola mudflow happened about 5600-5800 years ago and was one of the largest such volcanic events known in the world. Geologists estimate that about half a cubic mile (2.7 billion cubic yards) of debris from the summit of Mount Rainier, then about 16,000 feet above sea level, avalanched down the side of the volcano, moving down the valley in a series of incredibly massive surges. The valley around Federation Forest State Park was filled to a depth of at least 230 feet during this movement, and the valley floor at Silver Creek Ranger Station (14 miles further upstream) was temporarily buried under at least 300 feet of mud. The mudflow retained a high degree of fluidity all the way to the drift plains of the Puget Sound lowlands. Gigantic boulders, cobbles, and other debris carried in a deep river of mud were dammed temporarily at valley constrictions, creating inundations behind. Near Enumclaw, the large boulders were grounded as the mudflow thinned; but the fluid matrix of finer debris continued flowing seaward. Geologists speculate that the whole event lasted from several hours to a few days. When finally emplaced, the Osceola mudflow had the consistency of a wet concrete mixture; later, it dried and solidified.

The valley forests along Tahoma Creek knew little of Takobed's destructive whimsies. Eight hundred years ago the trees had found nearly perfect conditions for growth. But even when these towering specimens of Douglas-fir, western hemlock, and western redcedar were only fast-growing seedlings, the stage for their destruction was being prepared in the cold, icy climates high on the volcano.

A long series of wet years produced layer upon layer of heavy snow on the catchments of the Puyallup and Tahoma glacial basins. Only a fraction of each winter's snow melted off during the brief summers, and the lower layers of snow became ever more densely packed and eventually became part of the glacial masses themselves. Great channels of andesitic rock were being plucked from the steep summit slopes of the volcano as these glaciers moved downslope. Rock debris removed from the bedrock centuries before was emerging at the advancing fronts of the glaciers.

By now the trees in Tahoma Creek valley had grown into very tall poles. A long period of warmer climate had begun. While the Douglas-firs and hemlocks were recording an extended series of wide tree rings, indicating good growth, the Tahoma and South Tahoma glaciers were retreating. The terminal and lateral moraines marked their greatest advances; elsewhere these glaciers relinquished their burdens of andesitic rubble as they wasted away, and a thick drift filled the valley floor and lower slopes at the alpine elevations. When especially warm years were preceded by wet winters, torrents of water from melting snow and ice would erode deep channels through the

[1] Takhoma is one of the Northwest Indian names for Mount Rainier; Takobed is another name for the volcano.

drifts and moraines. A rocky wasteland extended for miles below the glacier terminus: a jumble of boulders, cobbles, gravels, and silts. Here and there were dangerously steep piles of rubble, undercut by runoff, and hanging in ever more precarious balance from one year to the next.

On this spring day in March, as the forests far below were approaching their 800th year, nothing of the unstable moraine and drift fields of the alpine valley could be seen. They lay under wet snow upon which an incessant, warm rain was falling, as it had for many days. The main channel of Tahoma Creek was swollen to capacity, and still the milky waters rose. Large trees were beginning to topple into the torrent as the banks were cut away. In the dreary, gray distances, ominous rumbles were heard as saturated heaps of rubble began slumping. Centuries of preparation had at last brought about a critical combination of rock, ice, snow, and water.

The mudflow began at night. A huge cavern had formed in the terminal lobe of the South Tahoma Glacier. Near midnight, an ice block over a hundred feet thick broke from the roof of this cavern. The block was awkwardly transported downstream by the outwash torrent, grounding for good about a half mile below the terminus. Within minutes, sediments carried by the meltwaters were deposited against this block. The dammed waters quickly backed up against the delicately hung rubble heaps deposited centuries before. A portion of the lateral moraine collapsed, and incredible volumes of rock poured into the impounded waters. This surge of rock debris and meltwater almost instantly overwhelmed the ice dam. The turbulent wall of rocks, water, and ice chunks now began a thunderous descent into Tahoma Valley. Greased and lubricated by the meltwaters over which it passed, and accelerated by steep slopes, the mudflow attained tremendous velocity. A dull roar and trembling ground preceded the mudlfow crest by only a few minutes and provided the only warning of the terror about to destroy every living thing in its path.

Rock avalanches occurring on volcanic slopes and mobilized by large amounts of water are called lahars. This term also refers to the material that finally comes to rest after such an event. All the major valleys around the Mount Rainier volcano contain the deposits of at least one lahar. Lahars originate in a variety of ways. Some are caused by volcanic eruptions or take place shortly there after. Others, like the one described above, are not related to eruptions. The Round Pass mudflow, for example, began as a massive rock avalanche or series of avalanches somewhere in the vicinity of Sunset Amphitheater. As these rocks

accelerated off the volcanic slopes they acquired enough water, ice, and snow to become a fluid mass, or lahar. Geologists prefer the term lahar to mudflow because the latter implies a certain textural consistency, whereas lahars generally contain wide variations of rock sizes, from enormous boulders to sands, silts, and clays.

By the gray, misty dawn the extent and aftermath of the lahar was revealed. Below Emerald Ridge the north side of the valley was covered by six feet of rubble. As the wave of the mudflow hurled itself down the valley, it obliterated everything and left a wake of glistening mineral debris up to 20 feet thick on the valley floor. Centuries later, geologists would here discover ancient logs four feet in diameter. Boulders up to six feet thick punctuated the surface of the mudflow. The flow thinned where the valley floor gentled and broadened near the confluence with the Nisqually River. About three miles above this confluence, a few trees yet stood. Along the floodplain of Tahoma Creek, a persistent drizzle washed the crowns of standing patriarchs and dripped onto the oozing flows of the new forest floor—no longer covered with mosses and ferns, but raw earth with a texture like wet cement.

The ancient Tahoma Creek mudflow of our scenario was a rather small event in the dynamic landscape around Mount Rainier. Not so, however, was the Round Pass mudflow about 2800 years ago. This mudflow contains clays that originated from the continuous steaming and chemical breakdown of minerals, which then cooled and solidified in a former throat of the volcano. Such are the rocks of Sunset Amphitheater. Very large rock avalanches of the scale of the Round Pass mudflow were probably formed exclusively by mass wasteage of these more or less chemically altered rocks. That mudflow deposited 200 million cubic yards of volcanic debris in the Puyallup River drainages, and lesser amounts in the Tahoma Creek drainage. Deposits of yellowish material still exist today, about 25 feet thick at Round Pass, and outcrops of the mudflow can be seen along the trail to Lake George.

The volume of the Round Pass mudflow was enough to temporarily fill the upper South Puyallup and Tahoma Creek valleys with at least 1000 feet of material. Directly north of Klapatche Park, the remnants of the mudflow reach a maximum height of 350 feet above the valley. Just outside the park, a thin veneer of the mudflow coats valley walls as high as 240 feet above the river. The Round Pass mudflow underlies much of the Puyallup River valley from the mouth of Deer Creek to the mouth of LeDoux Creek, about 10 miles from the park. In places the river has cut a trench as deep as 100 feet through this mudflow fill, and it is likely that still more fill underlies the floor of the Puyallup River valley for an unknown distance below the confluence with LeDoux Creek.

In Tahoma Creek, the Round Pass mudflow is about 20 feet thick about a mile above the former picnic area. Since its emplacement about 2800 years ago, at least three more lahars and some flood deposits have been added to that surface; but river downcutting has resulted in the present channel being about 20 feet below the rubble of the Round Pass mudflow. In order to reconstruct the return of forests on that ancient lahar terrace, we use the example provided by the Kautz Creek mudflow.

The Kautz Creek mudflow took place the night of 2-3 October 1947. Heavy rains fell that night. A cloudburst on the upper drainage basin, already saturated by precipitation, probably triggered the flow.

On the evening of 2 October, high waters washed out the bridge along the entrance road. The first mudflow arrived around 11 p.m., accompanied by a dull roar and vibrating ground. Successive flows took place during the night. Much of the flowage along the upper reaches of the creek was confined to the deep trench that had been cut previously by floodwaters. The floodplain of the lower valley, however, was covered with 25 to 30 feet of cobbly mudflow debris.

The trees of the lower valley, not far from the confluence with the Nisqually River, were smothered under the burden of mud. To be sure, the crowns for some weeks gave little sign of dying. But the root systems that laced the old forest soils were now buried some feet below the new ground surface. The delicate microscopic root hairs and associated fungal threads so necessary for the absorbent functions of the trees were now starving for oxygen in the cold, saturated soils at these deeper depths. As the roots died, so did the

Figure 30. Aerial view of a portion of the 1947 Kautz Creek mudflow, taken 24 August 1961. (Photo courtesy National Park Service)

Figure 31. Kautz Creek in flood, 23 August 1961. The stream is carrying a heavy load of sediment. (Photo courtesy National Park Service)

stems and crowns. But even as the needles began to fall, they were accompanied by an invisible rain of new life, the airborne spores and seeds of pioneering plants. And when the floodwaters of Tahoma Creek returned to their new channel, the very fine sands and silts left behind included among their grains these spores and seeds, carried by water and now planted in the ooze.

By outward appearance, the valley landscape that following growing season was austere—a geological mantle of cobbles and sand and grizzled, dying tree carcasses. Closer study, however, might reveal fringes of green around cobbles and boulders and here and there soil crusts of algae or lichens. The green fringes were mosses and the thallus-like growth forms of young ferns. By the end of the first year a few vascular plants had appeared. Many were annuals like willow-herb, *gayophytum*, or bent grasses. Perennial

plants were there, too: scattered seedlings of willow and black cottonwood from seeds blown in during early summer. Nevertheless, these were but tiny clues to the explosion of life that would follow the next year.

The second growing season began healing in earnest this scarred valley. Under, in, and on the winter snows of the first year were millions of dormant spores and seeds blown, washed, or carried during the previous fall and winter — plus some produced by last year's invaders. When the snow melted, a soft and very faint living hue was cast upon the gray, cobbled surface. Nearly everywhere the renewal of life began very modestly with mosses and lichens. Two pioneers are noteworthy: a tufted moss that botanists call *Racomitrium canescens*, and a gray lichen, called *Stereocaulon*, whose bizarre, erect fruiting branches give it stunning beauty. In this crunchy world of tiny plants some taller flowering herbs stand out. Here and

A

B

Figure 32. Repeat photographs of the 1947 Kautz Creek mudflow: (A) 1952 and (B) 1978 in which alders and mosses now dominate the site and saplings of Douglas-fir are common. (Photos courtesy University of Washington)

there are fireweed, pearly everlasting, white hawk-weed, spotted catsear, willow weed, and several kinds of hardy grasses and grasslike plants. Some red huckleberry seedlings became established near standing dead trees and downed logs. Most of these plants are opportunists that thrive in sunny, open locations. A disturbance is their bread and butter. Perhaps the disturbance need not be as catastrophic as this mudflow, but the fact remains that such plants persist only because disturbances keep happening.

These plants have another essential quality that enables them to be pioneers. They can grow on extremely infertile ground. This stony mineral substrate can hardly be termed soil; it lacks organic matter, has none of the structure or porosity identified with soil (in fact it is very dense and compact), and is deficient in mineral nutrition. One of the most serious deficiencies is soil nitrogen. These moss, herb, and grass pioneers effectively tolerate this almost sterile environment. They seem to require only sunny space and some kind of rooting medium, and there's plenty of that in this desert between the dead trees. By the very existence of these plants, however, the mudflow soil was being almost imperceptibly changed. Now a slight accretion of organic matter was developing on the surface of the soil and at shallow depths. The chemistry of the soil was being made a bit more favorable for plant growth, and soil aeration had improved near the surface. But these changes were still so minor that by the end of the second year they scarcely warrant mention. Only inches below the surface, the mineral rubble was still raw, compact, and infertile.

The life of a red alder begins as a tiny, winged nutlet about one millimeter wide. The seed germinates best on mineral rather than humic soil. In moist, warm valley-bottom locations, the sprouts grow rapidly and reach breast height the first year. Growth is slower on dry or shaded microsites. Once established, the alders can grow as rapidly as five feet per year, with sapling height growth most rapid during the first decade. At 20 years of age, stands of red alder may be 50 feet tall on wet sites, 30 or 40 feet on drier sites.

The importance of alder in early stages of plant succession on nutrient-poor, newly deposited geological substrate lies in its previously mentioned ability to fix atmospheric nitrogen. On such sites as this, alder in forest succession is comparable to legumes in cropped agricultural soils. The abundant atmospheric nitrogen, unusable by most plants, is fixed in the nodules of alder roots to organic forms, available to plants. Such nodules are specialized, symbiotic associations of root tissues and bacteria. Much of the

nitrogen fixed by the bacteria of the nodules is taken up by the growing alder and appears in the leaves. Decomposition of this nitrogen-rich leaf material in the litter is an important source of soil nitrogen for other plants. The symbiotically-fixed nitrogen also enters the soil through direct excretion from living alder roots. Fully stocked alder stands that are two to 15 years old can fix nitrogen at rates of about 300 pounds per acre per year. At the end of 15 years the quantity of organic and mineral nitrogen in these stands has been estimated between 3.5 and 7 tons per acre.

From the fourth to about the thirty-third year much of the mudflow remained under herbaceous dominance. The renewed plant life was a patchwork of easily contrasted plant communities. On some sites the compact, cobbly soils allowed only mosses and lichens, with a smattering of alders. Red and Sitka alders were most dense in the slight depressions and drainageways where runoff waters carried in and watered the seeds. However the most significant factor affecting revegetation was a legacy from the former forest. In areas where snags still remained and where down logs were plentiful bracken fern was now conspicuous, and both alder and salal were dense. Salal probably appeared when bear, deer, and small mammals ventured onto the mudflow using the alder patches to browse, graze, or hide. Their droppings carried viable seeds of the delicious berries foraged from nearby forests. A few of these shaded thickets were beginning to get enough soil buildup that plants such as oak fern and twinflower, more at home in mature forests, were now present. Total soil nitrogen in the upper horizon within these thickets (where organic matter was accumulating) was two or three times greater than in the upper soil of the moss-lichen community. Soil development, accelerated by decaying wood of the former forest, was preparing the way for subsequent events.

Actually the events were already in progress, but in the profusion of herbs and shrubs, it went unnoticed except by ants and small rodents. On the soil surface and among the "wet" mosses of these sites (that by now replaced *Racomitrium*) were the humble beginnings of the new forest. A few germinates of Douglas-fir, western white pine, and western hemlock became established as early as the second or third year. But it was year five that witnessed the greatest densities of Douglas-fir due to bumper crops of cones in nearby forests. The beginnings were not easy, for summer soil drought was taking heavy toll of tender seedlings. Most seeds fell on sterile soils, dominated by mosses and lacking the necessary mycorrhizal fungi for tree germinates to develop good roots. Conifer seeds had best chance if they fell near the "carry over" of logs and snags from the destroyed forest. Soil near a decaying log contains a bit more soil water in the hot, dry month of August. Perhaps more critical to the new seedling, however, was seedbed preparation by rodents. Rodents? Many foresters think of rodents as critters that kill seedlings by clipping, and otherwise have little use except as owl bait. Well, they can kill some seedlings, true. But squirrels, chipmunks, and other small mammals also feed on fungi in nearby forest stands. Moving into the mudflow along the shelter and pathways afforded by down logs, these animals leave urinary spots and fecal droppings that are perfect fertilizers for young roots needing rapid connection with mycorrhizal fungi for mineral nutrition on these otherwise deficient soils. In balance, rodents contribute far more to site preparation for a tree crop than the small toll taken from clipping. They are a critical link in nature's reforestation, which may help explain why after thirty-three years there are more seedling and sapling conifers in plant communities associated with the snag patches than there are in open areas.

The new forest on this mudflow was developing primarily by nature's prodigal device of overwhelming profusion— the saturation of the area by billions of seeds of which only a tiny fraction would survive. Thus, hidden under the stems and shade of bracken fern, pearly everlasting, fireweed, salal, and red alder, most of the seedlings died. But not all. After their first summer the survivors were only about a half-inch tall and had as much leaf surface as a salal berry. What these tiny beings needed was lots of luck, good genetics—and speed.

In forest populations, as with so many other affairs of life, the race belongs to the swift. Whoever gets there first wins. For seedling conifers one of the critical factors is light; once past the tenderest period (when the heat associated with direct sunlight can kill them), the more light the better. Douglas-fir and western white pine are particularly demanding. Western hemlock and western redcedar can get along with less, but even they grow best where light intensities approach full sun. Whoever can command the most sunlight can also shade his neighbor—and win. A year or two headstart might make the difference. For seedlings of equal age there is no dallying. To be shaded is, sooner or later, to perish. If one seedling can tap a better source of nitrogen-rich soil than its neighbor or germinates near a rodent pellet where it will get a quick inoculation of growth enriching mycorrhizae, so be it. If a seedling germinates under dense herbs, while a frog jump away another thrives in

a sunfleck, that's fate. If a seedling is slower-growing than its neighbor because of drier soil or because it is delayed by an extra inch of snowpack—well, too bad. All's fair in the war of growth. Five or eight hundred years down the line, perhaps as many as 20 Douglas-firs will command the overstory on this acre of mudflow, but right now a hundred thousand of them, descendants of a million seeds, are battling out the first round. And that says nothing of the other species. A precious few are destined to long, stalwart life; others will perish along the way. The deadly race has begun.

It took four or five years for aspiring seedlings to begin poking their terminal leaders above the salal canopy. In the thickets of red alder the trees were growing faster, for these sites were moister and nutritionally richer. But the alder itself was taller, so the conifers had to endure many years of shade before they emerged into full sunlight. Few persisted; most succumbed. The lower Tahoma Creek valley now presented a strange visage. Projecting high above the mudflow were massive gray skeletons of the forest buried 42 years earlier. Many of the dead trees already had toppled as their roots rotted; those yet standing had sloughed off their bark and all but a few of the larger limbs. They towered above a jungle of conifer thickets now asserting dominance eight to ten feet above the ground. This young and vigorous forest formed a bristly, rising tide of greenery. Stiff as fixed bayonets were the terminal branches of Douglas-fir and western white pine reaching for ever more sunlight. Droopy but equally determined were the terminal leaders of western hemlock. Occasional black cottonwood, Scouler's willow, or wild cherry would be found growing as rapidly as the conifers. But young forest did not yet completely cover the mudflow. At the very cobbly or the hottest, driest locations a mossy turf still dominated. Where sands were eroded or reworked by runoff only scattered shrubs were growing. A few locations still were controlled by heavy shrub cover and herbs beneath, with only a few trees proclaiming a winning struggle against the suppressive surroundings.

In following years the forest continued to grow at the rate of about one foot annually. More trees gradually became established in the openings, although their growth rates were often much slower, especially on the cobbly, mossy sites. As dense sapling thickets grew, the understory became heavily shaded, and shrubs thinned. Some of the pioneering herbs disappeared from sites they once dominated. Other herbs, mostly perennials with long-lived root systems such as bracken fern, were now just scattered individuals here and there in the shade of the thickets. Among the cobbles of the more moist locations a few oak ferns and other shade-tolerant plants could now be found.

Mudflows have repeatedly welled down Kautz Creek during the last 4000 years, burying forests and soils. After each event a new forest began. Forest succession on Kautz Creek today probably differs in detail from the succession that occurred along nearby lower Tahoma Creek 2800 years ago, because the climates and environments are not identical. We can, therefore, only speculate that the similarities in recolonization of a mudflow outweigh the differences.

Forty or so years after the Kautz Creek mudflow another coniferous forest has replaced the one destroyed. On the aggraded fan along the road the park visitor can see dense sapling stands. Common species are Douglas-fir and western hemlock, but individuals of nearly every tree species present in the park can be found here. Light intensities are very low under the conifer thickets, and the understory is generally sparse. The more open areas and disturbance sites give clues to stages of plant succession that preceded the conifers.

About two miles upstream the valley is cooler and possibly wetter. Sitka alder replaces red alder as part of the shrub stage of succession. There is no salal. Douglas-fir is somewhat less important in the new forest, and subalpine fir and mountain hemlock are more plentiful.

And so, forty years after that fateful October day, the next generation of trees was growing rapidly and vigorously in the valley. The cycle had been completed. And just as the older forest was doomed, so too the new. Geological and biological forces have, to this day, alternated and conflicted in this valley arena, each as inevitable as the other. As the giant volcano wastes away in convulsive episodes, so in response the forests patiently heal the scarred land-scapes of the lower elevations.

Figure 33. Mount Rainier from Yakima Meadows.

80

Chapter 7
Glaciers

The whiteness of the Mount Rainier summit is one of its most alluring attributes. Whether seen from afar as a brilliant beacon on a clear day or from close up as a tortured terrain of deep fissures and seracs, the glaciers of the volcano can evoke wonder, awe, fear, or a sense of grandeur. For hundreds of thousands of years, long before the Rainier volcanic cone was formed, glaciers and forests have been at war. What appears to us as the proper order of nature—the snow and ice slopes above, the skirts of forest below—is but a transitory state in the battle between ice and trees. Only a narrow zone of rock rubble and subalpine parkland separates the adversaries. Today the forests are about as far up the volcano's slopes as they have ever been, and correspondingly the glaciers are remnant vestiges of those awesome icecaps that almost buried the entire Cascade Range. In this chapter we will travel from a time about 75,000 years ago, the latter part of the Ice Age, to the present. The conflict between ice and forest, we shall see, has vacillated over a broad geographic and elevational front.

Ice Comes and Goes

About 75,000 years ago the Mount Rainier volcano had reached its present size, but was burdened with huge masses of ice that entirely covered its flanks and reached down the valleys to the lowlands in great white tongues. The lowlands also were covered by ice from another source. A vast ice sheet blanketed much of western British Columbia. This sheet, nurtured by the expansion of glaciers from the coastal mountains of British Columbia, formed a huge lobe that advanced southward into the Puget Sound lowlands of western Washington. Geologists call this period of glacial maxima the Salmon Springs Glaciation. Average July temperatures during the first of the two great ice advances that comprise this glaciation were about 5° to 7°C lower than they are now. To appreciate the significance of this, let us note that an average Cascade Range difference in July temperatures between tundra and sea-level elevations is about 7°C. In effect, a 5° to 7°C temperature drop would lower the timberlines to almost present-day sea level! With ice covering the lowlands (the southern limit of the Puget Lobe during Salmon Springs Glaciation is not precisely known, but

it probably reached somewhere in the vicinity of Olympia) and alpine glaciers covering the valleys and slopes of the Cascades, the region around Mount Rainier had a polar appearance. At the lowest elevations, climates marginal to the glaciers (sometimes called periglacial climates) probably supported a treeless vegetation known as tundra: hardy mosses and lichens, grasses and sedges, and perhaps some low, mat-forming shrubs. There were no forests.

About 72,000 years ago a regional warming trend began. Mean July temperatures increased to about 2°C colder than present, the ice flows retreated, and the deglaciated lowlands became revegetated. Near Tacoma, pollen sequences from a peat sample tell the story. At first the vegetation of the raw cobbles, sands, and silts left behind by the glaciers (the mineral debris deposited by melting glaciers is known as drift) consisted of a frigid-climate tundra. A similar vegetation today can be found, for example, on Burroughs Mountain. The sedge- and grass-dominated areas gradually developed into forests of pine and spruce (Sitka spruce is a common coastal species) and subsequently into still warmer forests of western hemlock and true fir. The climate never became mild enough to accommodate the Douglas-fir forests that are so common today in the Puget Sound lowlands. This unglaciated forest interval was brief: regional temperatures again dropped, and the Puget Lobe readvanced. Tundra vegetation replaced the forest, and the pollen record was interrupted when glaciers and their resultant drift again blanketed the land. In the mountains, the snowline (the elevation above which snow continues from one winter to the next) may have dropped as low as about 3000 feet. Below this line, great tongues of ice licked the land. For thousands of years western Washington was again locked in perennial winter.

The Salmon Springs Glaciation ended with a pronounced global warming that lasted several thousand years—the Olympia Interglaciation. The rubble of boulders and rocks left behind as the glaciers melted are deeply weathered. At Mount Rainier the extent of this rubble, known as the Hayden Creek and Wingate Hill drift, gives evidence of the length of some of the alpine glaciers that existed during the Salmon Springs glacial maxima. Down the Cowlitz, for example, a single glacier extended some 65 miles from the

*Figure 34. Only a narrow zone of rock rubble separates the adversaries.
Lodgepole pine and subalpine fir on the moraine of Emmons Glacier.*

volcano to somewhere about 33 miles west of Randle. The great mass of these glaciers can be appreciated by noticing the size of such U-shaped valleys as the Cowlitz, Nisqually, Carbon River, or White River. These U-shaped valleys are the channels in which the ice flowed.

Forest vegetation occupied the valleys and lower mountain slopes during the warmer episodes of the Olympia Interglaciation. But the mean July temperatures were nevertheless not more than 2° to 3°C below those of the present, which meant that the timberlines were about 1300 to 1600 feet lower than they are now. The high Cascades still resembled a jagged deep freeze.

The last major period when glaciers occupied both the mountains and lowlands of western Washington is the Fraser Glaciation, which extended roughly from 25,000 to 10,800 years ago. The period began with a renewed growth of alpine glaciers. A terminal moraine near the mouth of Evans Creek in the Carbon River valley marked a great advance of the Carbon Glacier, perhaps 19,000 years ago.

The climatic episode during which the alpine glaciers reached their maximum extent and deposited drifts in the mountains of western Washington is known as the Evans Creek Stade. Regional snowlines near Mount Rainier were probably between 4300 and 4500 feet elevation, and ice fields doubtlessly existed at these elevations and along the crest of the range southeast of Mount Rainier. Within the present-day park boundaries, all but the highest ridges and divides were under ice.

Where were the forests during this time? They were mostly along the coastal plains at some distance from the glacial fronts. Pollens from a bog near Humptulips (on the Olympic Peninsula) consist mostly of lodgepole pine and grasses, with lesser amounts of Sitka spruce, western hemlock, and mountain hemlock. Botanists speculate that the vegetation on parts of the ice-free Olympic Peninsula must have appeared somewhat like the present-day Pacific coast of Alaska, where Sitka spruce and mountain hemlock forests adjoin the grassy meadows and tundras of the higher elevations. Forests were not widespread on the lowlands west of the Cascade Range, however, because even as the alpine glaciers of the Evans Creek Stade were retreating, another advance of the Puget Lobe was pushing southward into the lowland. At its climax, the Puget Lobe terminated about 15 miles south of Olympia sometime around 15,000 years ago. A climatic episode known as the Vashon Stade (not quite synchronous to the Evans Creek Stade) gave rise to an ice mass that reached a

thickness of about 3,000 feet in the Seattle area. Average July temperatures at Humptulips dropped to about 11°C, about 6° below today's July mean (which is 17°C). Pollen spectra suggest a cold-tolerant forest of mountain hemlock and less abundance of western hemlock compared to the preceding forest. Lodgepole pine was a common constituent of forests near Humptulips during both the Evans Creek and Vashon stades.

The alpine glaciers around Mount Rainier began to recede sometime before 15,000 years ago while the ice of the Puget Lobe was still expanding in the lowlands. This anomaly apparently was initiated by regional warming that began prior to the maximum growth of the Puget Lobe. But as the mountain glaciers retreated, leaving behind the Evans Creek Drift, the Cordilleran ice sheet was nurtured and continued to grow due to increases of precipitation turning to snow and ice in the locally maintained cold climate on its massive surface. Eventually, the Puget Lobe reached its southern limit before it too began to retreat under the warmer climate. Sometime before 13,500 years ago it had melted from the Seattle area. Lowlands in the vicinity of Bellingham, formerly under ice, were inundated by shallow marine seas.

During this warming episode (the Everson Interstade), the pollen record at the bog near Humptulips again reveals an increase in western hemlocks and true firs in adjoining forests, although lodgepole pine was still, as it continued to be throughout the Fraser Glaciation, the major pollen contributor here. There was no Douglas-fir. The timberlines in the mountains may have climbed to about 3000-3500 feet elevation. The glaciers around Mount Rainier continued to recede until about 11,000 years ago, at which time there was about as much ice as there has been during the last century.

Just before the Fraser Glaciation ended, a third cold oscillation of climate occurred—the Sumas Stade. The glaciers again grew from their positions in the ice-carved basins, or cirques, of the upper valleys. The Sumas Stade was rather minor and short-lived. The glaciers never again attained the massiveness and scale they had during the Salmon Springs and earlier stades of the Fraser Glaciation.

The climate and environment of a late Pleistocene glacial recession can be experienced at Mount Rainier. A hike into the drift basin of the Emmons Glacier takes us back 15,000 years. As we walk along the trail from the White River Campground, we pass through stands of Engelmann spruce and subalpine fir. These trees are common at the highest forested elevations in the Rocky Mountains; but the spruce, in particular, is an uncommon tree in the Cascades. Why then their abundance here?

Other plants along this trail also suggest a cold, continental climate—more like the high Rockies than the Pacific Cascades. There may be several reasons why the upper basin of the White River reveals a frigid, subpolar climate. This sector of the Rainier volcanic cone faces northeast and thus receives less overall solar radiation and warmth than the other sectors. It is also drier than the westerly slopes of the cone which are under the partial rain shadow of Mount Rainier. Rocky Mountain forests of Engelmann spruce and subalpine fir grow in colder, drier climates than Cascade forests.

Equally important, perhaps, are the mass and geometry of the major glaciers. The Emmons Glacier descends almost two vertical miles from the summit of Mount Rainier. Because of this enormous ice mass, the air at the glacier's surface has a large flow area for heat exchange. Refrigerated air along this surface slides down into the valley and reduces the night temperatures there, shifting the climate of the upper basin to a more continental extreme.

And what does this have to do with the climates of the Pleistocene? Consider the principal pollen sources recorded in peat and bog samples during the glacial recessions of the Salmon Springs and Fraser glaciations. The Salmon Springs peat sample near Tacoma, mentioned earlier, shows a brief period of spruce and pine pollen, which was preceded by tundra and followed by western hemlock-true fir forest. One difficulty, however, concerns pollen identification. Some botanists refer to the Pleistocene-aged spruce pollens as Engelmann spruce, and others as Sitka spruce. Apparently there is no problem with pollen identification of mountain hemlock, western hemlock, and lodgepole pine. We certainly have no problem here in the upper White River drainage: the trees before us definitely are Engelmann spruce, subalpine fir, and lesser numbers of mountain hemlock and silver fir. Both of these firs are included in the "true firs" of the Pleistocene pollen descriptions. The crucial point is this: here at 4600 feet is a forest of spruce, mountain hemlock, and "true fir" whose composition may be similar to another forest 72,000 years ago that was contributing pollen to a peaty flat at 246 feet elevation near present-day Tacoma.

But something is missing from this periglacial forest of the White River Valley where we have been walking. Yes, there are numerous different trees here, but didn't we mention that lodgepole pine was also one of the major pollen sources of those peat deposits dating 25,000 to 10,800 years B.P. (the late Pleistocene)?

We continue on and soon cross the footbridge over Interfork Creek. The trail pitches steeply as we labor onto the bouldery rubble of the Emmons moraine. Tall trees are left behind; the landscape is a raw nightmare of rocks and boulders, some of which were deposited in a massive rock avalanche from Little Tahoma Peak in 1963. The immensity of this terrain, pocked by scores of rubble heaps, ridges, troughs, and gravelly channels, is impressive. Perhaps a mile distant looms the threatening black terminus of the Emmons. We can be comforted by the thought that it is retreating, for only 89 years ago (1900) ice covered the site where we stand.

Young trees are colonizing this bouldery area. We see saplings of subalpine fir, Engelmann spruce, mountain hemlock, and Sitka alder. About 980 feet east is a series of terminal moraines deposited by the glacier. A rather dense sapling forest has become established there; some of the oldest trees germinated within a few years after the morainal rubble was no longer subject to scouring and abrasion from glacial meltwaters. But what's this? Look at the hundreds of lodgepole pine among the Engelmann spruce, sub-alpine fir, and mountain hemlock!

Our discovery of the lodgepole pine so close to the Emmons terminus, colonizing ground recently vacated by ice, is quite exciting. According to the authoritative botanist, Henry P. Hansen, this pine was the primary invader near ice front margins of the Puget Sound lowlands during the end of the Fraser Glaciation. Pollen profiles at Puget Sound locations during glacial recessions typically show mixtures of lodgepole pine, "spruce," mountain hemlock, and alder—all of which we see around us. Pollen sediments now accumulating in nearby lakes and ponds might resemble (if we overlook contamination from forests of warmer slopes and exposures) the pine-spruce-mountain hemlock pollen assemblages of the late Pleistocene. Our hike from the White River Campground has taken us into the Ice Age; this awareness heightens the sense of unreality that has accompanied us ever since we scrambled onto the morainal surface below the Emmons Glacier.

Let's examine how these crescent-shaped terminal moraines become forested. On one of them, the pith rings of oldest trees date to the years 1750, 1785, 1749, and 1755. The Emmons ice started to recede here around 1745. A parallel crescentric contour about 330 feet up the valley contains trees germinated in 1864, 1850, and 1855, and indicates the position of the Emmons Glacier about 100 years later. The glacier was melting faster now, because the next 50 to 75 years witnessed a recession of about 490 feet.

84

Some of the saplings on the 1900 moraine we crossed earlier had germinated as early as 1902 and 1905. From those years to the present, the retreat of the Emmons Glacier has been astonishingly rapid. Some climatologists have suggested that the global temperatures of the last century have been higher than any time during the previous half million years. It's very likely that such wasting of the once mighty Emmons is being driven by the warming trend of the past hundred years.

We sit on a boulder and contemplate the glacier at the far end of this rubbled trough. All the events of the Ice Age that we have been reliving—great advances of ice crunching out forests and then retreating behind rubbled deposits of drift and glacial outwash—have occurred mostly in a lowland arena. The nearby lodgepole pines spearheading the periglacial advance of the forest are growing not at coastal elevations, but at 4900 feet. Only during the last 10,000 to 11,000 years has this upper glacial valley become deglaciated. Sharp declines of spruce pollen found in peat and bog samples indicate that the Fraser Glaciation ended about 10,800 years ago. This marked the beginning of the hypsithermal period—a period of regionally high temperatures—that lasted almost 7,000 years. On the Olympic Peninsula, the mean July temperatures gradually increased to almost 17°C, much higher than ever in the late Pleistocene. At the same time the precipitation declined, as evidenced in part by the increased importance of Douglas-fir as a coastal tree at the expense of western hemlock. This long period of relative warmth and dryness may have reduced the glaciers around this volcano to sizes smaller than now, and some might have disappeared altogether. The warm, dry period was not confined strictly to the Northwest. In Colorado it climaxed around 7500-6500 years ago, when alpine glaciers and perennial snowbanks disappeared and the vegetation zones were higher than they are today.

But climates never stand still. There may have been an interval that followed the hypsithermal in the Northwest when the temperatures again lowered but the winters remained comparatively dry. About 3500 years ago, the glaciers around Mount Rainier again advanced as the cold and wet climates returned. This marked the beginning of "neoglaciation" in the Northwest—two episodes of glacial advance separated by 1000 years. The glaciers grew from their cirque valleys at about 6500 feet elevation (these cirques had lower elevational limits around 4500 feet during the Fraser Glaciation) and became somewhat larger and longer than they are now. The first of the advances, known as the Burroughs Mountain Stade, lasted from 3500 to 2000 years B.P.; the second, the Garda Stade,

began in what is sometimes called the "Little Ice Age" because records of cold temperatures, poor crops, delayed grape harvests, and ice advances in Europe and North America are well documented. At Mount Rainier, the greatest advance of the Carbon Glacier during the Garda Stade is evidenced by a lateral moraine which now supports trees that germinated as early as 1217. Of course, those old trees germinated some unknown number of years after the glacier had reached maximum advance. In other valleys around the volcano, episodes of glacial expansion culminated at various times from the mid-14th to the mid-19th centuries, as judged by the ages of trees growing on their moraines.

Our wandering on the Emmons drift basin has revealed that this glacier is in rapid retreat. Another area of glacial retreat can be studied at the Nisqually River bridge near Nahunta Falls. When Lieutenant A. V. Kautz observed the Nisqually Glacier in 1857, the ice front was just about at the site of the modern bridge. However, many visitors would have trouble finding the terminus today because it is over a mile upstream from the bridge and covered with black rubble. In fact, the botanical evidence of the glacier's position in the mid-19th century is far more spectacular. When Kautz beheld it, the Nisqually Glacier already was melting back, and today we can see a sharp trimline of trees on the sides of the valley that marks the edge of the ice in 1840. Older trees above the trimline germinated between 1656-1690, and just below at the very edge are trees that date to 1842 and 1843. Lower in the valley and an easy walk from the bridge is a stand of silver fir, western hemlock, and Alaska yellow-cedar growing on drift—some of the larger trees germinated about 1855, probably within a few years after the glacier vacated. What seems so astonishing is the rapidity with which a closed forest has taken over on the raw rubble here. Did nutrients seep in from the forests above the trimline? Was the unusually warm climate since about 1850 partly responsible?

So far, we have been looking only at forests in the glacial valleys. In the subalpine parklands, visitors are usually dazzled by the color and fragrance of flowering meadows. Against the more distant background of plunging glaciers are fields of lupine, valerian, paintbrush, avalanche lilies, cinquefoil, fleabane, heather, grasses and sedges. Islands of wind-shaped trees contribute to the landscape pattern. These gently rolling uplands and their pleasing mosaics of trees and meadows mark the climatic tension zone between forests and tundra.

Cold, wet winters or short, cool summers are

Figure 35. Massive tree invasion of the parkland meadows has occurred in some locations, such as this one in Paradise Valley.

the ingredients of tundra-like climates...and the conditions that make glaciers grow. Mild winters, reduced snowfall, or long, warm summers encourage forest expansion into the forest-tundra borderlands. At the lower elevations, the glacial ice is melting away at a rate faster than the accumulation of snowfall that persists from one winter to the next at higher elevations. Indeed, the snowline at Mount Rainier moved up from about 5900 feet in 1910 to nearly 7600 feet in 1952. A negative annual ice mass budget sustained over a number of years causes the terminus of a glacier to retreat...and the forests to follow close behind. The trees are now chasing the glaciers.

The evidence of forest advance into meadow areas of the subalpine is all around, not just at Mount Rainier but throughout the Cascade Range of Oregon and Washington and in the Olympic Mountains. The regionalization of forest invasion suggests a climatic

cause, not just local influences such as grazing or fire. At Paradise and numerous other subalpine parklands (Spray Park, Indian Henry's Hunting Ground, Van Trump Park) we find massive invasions of trees into the flowering meadows. Seedlings and saplings of mostly subalpine fir are beginning to form thickets in the openings. Before long, the lupine and valerian will yield to such forest plants as rhododendron, trailing raspberry, or oval-leaf huckleberry.

Lest we get too unsettled about thoughts of disappearing meadows, let's look at the tree invasion more carefully. Some meadows have a high density of new seedlings and saplings; others have only a few or none. Often the higher the altitude the less extensive the recent invasions, but there are exceptions. Growth of established seedlings is fastest on warmer microsites. while suppressed growth is characteristic of the young trees in swales, depressions, and drainage-

Figure 36. Trees on prominent relief features in the subalpine parkland. Depth and duration of snowpack are critical for determining forest and meadow boundaries.

ways. However, the warmer microsites at Paradise exhibit the lowest densities of new trees; the wettest sites seem to have the highest densities.

Other apparent mosaics of trees and meadows in the subalpine are the trees on prominent relief features such as moraines and rocky outcrops with meadows in the basins between. The sharp rises usually contain trees that were growing long before the period of recent invasion, and there is often an abrupt boundary between forest and meadow.

The swing of the climatic pendulum is measured in the subalpine meadows by the depth and duration of snowpack. Cold years of deep snow prevent trees from invading and growing; but a series of warm years can open up areas of low relief for long enough growing seasons to accommodate trees. In fact, long warm summers might create conditions that are too dry for trees on certain south-facing upper slopes. In conjunction with herb competition, few seedlings become established, although those that do grow rapidly. Average or normal years also are inimical to trees except on the prominent relief where the snow is not very deep.

A massive wave of new trees into the sub-alpine meadows appeared mostly between 1928 and 1937. Since then, only a few have been able to invade. This establishment period coincided with the years when the Nisqually Glacier was losing its ice mass. After 1945 the glacier was accumulating mass or holding even. At elevations within the subalpine, the average snowpack depths of meadow areas doubtless increased after 1945. The climatic "window" that permitted subalpine fir and mountain hemlock to invade these meadows had closed. And trees in the swales and depressions were now subject to shorter growing seasons and longer intervals of cold, saturated soils; they therefore grew at painfully slow rates, barely surviving.

The subalpine parkland is fine-tuned to short-term climatic fluxes. The constant pressure of the forests to expand into meadows is held in check only by the degree of rigor imposed by the Pacific North-west tundra climate. Tree lines and forest borders will expand when the climates turn milder; if colder, we can anticipate a dieback of forest growth along tundra margins, suppression and death of seedlings under prolonged snowpack, and changes in the mosaic patterns of the various meadow communities in response to shorter growing seasons.

Our forests will always be linked to the great glaciers, for both are responding in an opposite manner to the changes of climate. The periglacial borders of the Mount Rainier volcano are a fascinating, ever-transient chronicle of the climates of the past, present, and future.

Outburst Floods

Rivers in flood are a terrifying spectacle, dangerous and destructive. The milky waters of Mount Rainier are even more so, for two reasons: the grades along which water rushes on this volcano are steep, and the glaciers at the headwaters harbor enormous quantities of water. When this water is released suddenly—watch out! A glacial outburst flood is not mere violence. It is stark, unmitigated wrath. The flood channels, we finally seem to be learning, are places to avoid, for nothing within is very permanent.

Consider this account, told to me by an enthusiast of the Rainier country... When his children were tiny, the family used to hike near the snout of the Carbon Glacier and picnic on a boulder the size of a small house. One spring they came—and the boulder was gone. Everyone was horrified by this example of the river's power. The children could never remember the name "Carbon"—instead, they called it "the river that changes all the time."

Even the rivers in "ordinary" high-water discharge can be impressive. I can recall standing at Sunshine Point in July 1965 and watching the high waters of the Nisqually flow by. From bank to bank, perhaps 200 yards wide then, there was a giddy flow of fast water whose unevenness—not whitewater here, but a pimpled, riffled surface—must have reflected the bumpiness of boulders and rocks along the bottom. Every so often, some re-launched jetsam would twist and bob along its way in deeper parts of the channel— an old cottonwood bole or some alder uprooted from an ephemeral river bar. Near the shore the current was slower. Small chunks of bank at the cutting edge of a turning channel were collapsing in mini-landslides; the sands and pebbles disappeared into gray mystery, their ripples swept downcurrent to merge among the waves and eddies of the surface. The river was making loud but muffled sounds against a drumming background that seemed to come from the bottom. From the deeper parts of the channels, I listened to the clicks, clunks, and clacks of cobbles rolling along the bottom and striking each other. Suddenly I realized that this was the sound of the polishing process whereby river rocks become rounded. Nothing along that serpentine channel bottom, whether sand grain or boulder, could be anything but spheroid.

Always before, when I had seen these round rocks, they were inert as sediments along the banks and floodplains. But here they were alive, a fantastic hidden motion of billions of odd-sized ball bearings tumbling toward the sea. I closed my eyes to better "see" with my ears the turbulence of the river bottom. It was easy to imagine the clacking channels as a kind of crazy roller derby over which the faster waters above were sliding—a continuous thread in a downhill race to the Pacific. Opening my eyes and returning to reality, I could appreciate the power of water that propelled so enormous a sediment load.

The quantity of meltwater issuing from a glacier depends on many factors, including the amount of snow and ice, air temperature, heat flux to the glacier surface by direct solar radiation or as precipitation, and heat absorption properties of the surface. When conditions are right the outburst floods can be devastating. Such floods came from the Nisqually Glacier in 1932, 1934, and 1955. Each was preceded by heavy rainfalls that caused water in the riverbed to reach limits of containment. The actual outbursts in each flood washed away the highway bridge. The surges of water and sediments on 25 October 1955 were powerful enough to rip out the heavily reinforced concrete abutment that supported an 80-foot highway span.

Is there any difference between a glacial outburst flood and a mudflow (Chapter 6)? To be sure, there's a fine line between the October 1955 flood and the 1947 Kautz mudflow. The causes of each of those events were rather similar. More generally, however, mudflows are rock avalanches that acquire water and become fluid; glacial outburst floods are water avalanches that acquire rocks and become slurries. The rocks of mudflows can originate almost anywhere on the volcanic cone, such as the chemically altered rocks near the summit. The rocks and other mineral sediments mobilized in floods originate mostly from the drift or from sediments in front of the glaciers, and from river channels and banks. However, it is pointless to quibble over the labeling of one of these mass-wasting or erosive geologic events; the destructive effects are far more important, and we would like to know the conditions and events that lead up to and trigger them.

Let's go back to the Nisqually River bridge, where we earlier looked at the 1840 trimline of the glacier. Another measure of the glacier is here: the size of its outburst flood channel. No...not the channel or system of braided channels in which the milky waters are now flowing...not the "normal" flow we see from the bridge as a mere trickle in the vastness of cobbled rubble. Look instead at the distance between the standing forests on each side. The abrupt forest margins are the flood trimlines; like a fisherman's hands, they tell us how big was the one that got away. Further evidence is provided by the fringe of debris lining the channel in front of the old trees—a debris dike of broken trees that were deposited when the flood levels subsided. What's more, some of the logs are big enough to suggest that trees more than a century and a half old were torn from their rootholds and deposited downstream.

But where did they come from, and what force uprooted them? Answers to these simple questions are complex and exciting. Pursuit of a plausible explanation will carry us into the fields of climatology, glaciology, river hydrology, and forest history, and will serve to illustrate the kind of detective work routinely engaged in by scientists who deal with the past.

Near the end of the Garda Stade, some several years prior to 1840, the Nisqually Glacier was going through three kinds of developmental stages. There were years when the glacier was advancing and years when the glacier was retreating. There also were periods when the glacier maintained its approximate position; that is, the melting at the ice terminus was more or less balanced by the forward flow of the glacier. The amount of time spent in each of these developmental stages, as well as the sequence of the stages, will be critical in our analysis of how those trees were uprooted and redeposited along the margins of the flood channel.

Two plausible hypotheses about those uprooted trees appear to be:

1. The big trees were torn by water from their positions inside the flood channel somewhere upstream.

2. The big trees in the path of the growing glacier were gouged out by ice and later deposited in a glacial outburst flood.

Can we choose the best hypothesis from the evidence on hand? Hypothesis no. 1 doesn't seem to fit the facts. If the big trees are really older than 150 years, they germinated before 1830 somewhere in the flood channel up from this bridge. But we know that ice occupied that area in 1840, and trees cannot live under ice. The clincher, of course, would be to count tree rings on a cross section of one of those logs to see if, in fact, it was older than 150 years.

What about hypothesis no. 2? Recall that the older trees above the glacier trimline were dated 1656-1690; they were 150-184 years old in 1840 when the ice began to retreat—old enough to fit the size and presumed age of some of those logs in the debris dikes. Is it possible that part of the same forest population also existed on valley slopes below the not-yet-formed ice trimline when the Nisqually Glacier was advancing? Glaciers can grow very rapidly. E. L. Ladurie, the chronologer of climates during the Little Ice Age, notes that officials in the Alps during the 1640s reported the Des Bois Glacier growing "by over a musket shot every day, even in the month of August." Trees in front would be bulldozed aside. Could a forest here in the Nisqually that was chasing a glacier sometime in the mid to late 17th century get trapped by a sudden, dramatic reversal of climate and have the glacier turn on it? Climatologists know that the Little Ice Age had both warm spells and cold ones—why not here at Mount Rainier? These possibilities are consistent with hypothesis no. 2. When the glacier occupied its maximum position as measured by the 1840 trimline and moraines, some of its ice might have been lined with tree-victims. When it started to retreat after 1840, the victims were dumped on moraine or drift to be picked up by glacial outwash and redeposited.

It is possible that the glacier maintained its approximate 1840 position for a certain length of time before retreating. For example, if climatic conditions were such that the glacier lingered here, say, for 40 years, then trees younger than the 1656-1690 population could have grown in the channel below the trimline for 110-144 years at most. The longer the glacier lingered, the shorter would be the time for young trees to grow in areas below the stationary glacier, and the smaller they would be when ripped out by flood waters. Some trees of the debris dikes might have originated when outburst floods cut away the banks of the Garda Drift that supported trees of the 1855 forest of silver fir, western hemlock, and Alaska yellow-cedar.

We cannot accept hypothesis no. 2 without some further poking around in those log dikes, obtaining some tree ring counts and taking some measurements on the juxtapositions of moraines, log positions, forest borders, and so forth. But our inquiry has been worthwhile. The best statements for interpreting the landscape are often in the form of questions. Simply by asking how those old, broken trees got here, we open the door to an exciting possibility. In the battle between glaciers and forests at Mount Rainier, we might be seeing some direct casualties in what amounts to hand-to-hand combat between ice and trees.

Ricksetter Point is another good place to look down on the Nisqually River. We again marvel at the breadth of the flood channel; just about everywhere are gravelly and bouldery bars that remind us of a bygone flood rampage. Some alders and willows have the temerity to trespass on forbidden terrain, blissfully unaware of the significance of the grayed, wooden hulk nearby. Seeds will sprout on favorable sites—and river bars are favorite locations for opportunists like alder, willow, and cottonwood. They might even sprout between railroad tracks since nothing in their set of genetic instructions has told them that a freight train might come barreling along sooner or later. As time progresses, the very edges of the flood channel will become relatively safe. As the water cuts ever deeper in the central channels of the river, ever more massive floods would be required to reach containment levels. The larger the floods, the less probable they become, and thus the chances for channel-edge tree survival improve.

But do you notice that remnant stand of dead trees about a half mile below the Nisqually Bridge? The dice of fate had their number during the glacial outburst flood of 1955. The trees were killed by abrasion from the rocks carried in the flood and by subsequent root burial under the sediment load deposited when the flood waters subsided. A segment of old forest venturing too far down the valley was amputated by flood. Those sharp lines of living trees along the banks tell us how big the floods have been not so long ago, and how big they might be again. More important, those lines of living trees and those dead trees tell us that this is no man's land. Below the glacier, all the signs of nature read, "This channel belongs to water and minerals only. Venture at your own risk!"

Many miles downstream only the silt-laden, milky waters are left to remind us of the glacial headwaters of the Nisqually. It is late summer now; the river is at low flow volume. (The lowest flow volume is in winter when everything is frozen up.) Just outside Sunshine Point Campground, the water laps against the sands and polished cobbles of the shore. Sharply cut banks mark the edge of a terrace, deposited perhaps two centuries ago by some unrecorded river rampage of glacier wastage. Across the river, tall black cottonwoods stand on a still higher terrace. At Sunshine Point itself, engineers have built an artificial boulder jetty into the river; I wonder how long it will last?

On the terrace nearby is a forest of the WESTERN HEMLOCK/DEVIL'S CLUB type, shaded and inviting on this summer day. Tall black cottonwoods are common. Red alder and big leaf maple are growing on sands and cobbles of the old floodplain. Underneath are young western hemlock, western redcedar, and occasional specimens of grand fir. The shade-spangled understory is a profusion of vine

Figure 37. Valley forests killed by burial and alluvial abrasion after glacial outburst flooding below the Nisqually Glacier.

maple, elderberry, currant, and trailing blackberry. A dense spread of Oregon wood sorrel, sword fern, lady fern, enchanter's nightshade, sweet cicely, bedstraw, betony, waterleaf, and silvergreen becomes homogenized into a textured carpet that hides the geologic deposit beneath. On a sleepy summer afternoon, it seems absurd to think about the idea of glaciers on the rampage...or that this forest links its destiny by a milky thread to the antics of an unpredictable ice mass...or that, not so long ago, this very site was buried under hundreds of feet of ice.

Absurd they may seem, but the fact remains: this stand of trees and undergrowth at Sunshine Point is just an instant of time, no more, no less.

Chapter 8
Old Growth

The first great fact about conservation is that it stands for development.

In the second place conservation stands for the prevention of waste.
—*Gifford Pinchot*

Some of the oldest trees in the park are far up on the headwaters of Ipsut Creek. The trail starts climbing out of the Carbon River valley through forests containing scattered Douglas-fir whose breast height diameters are about five feet. These trees are approximately 550 years old. Some large and tall western hemlock and silver fir are also encountered. These stalwart ancients refuse to be crowded by their peers. Each tree has its own space and privacy; the canopy is rather open. The aggressive and irrepressible younger generation of hemlock and silver fir refuses to be awed by the stature of the old trees; these youngsters brashly assert their upward rights and ignore the spaced decorum of the elders. It is as well, for when an elder dies, which is inevitable, its canopy space will soon be taken by the tallest, most heavily foliaged contender among the rising generation of upstarts. While the political in-fighting for ascendancy to the local throne is intense among the understory

Figure 38. Ancient Alaska yellow-cedar in the Ipsut Creek basin.

trees, the result is an orderly, continuous, and predictable sequence of forest maintenance. This process of mortality and replacement, so evident among tree populations of old-growth stands, is called gap phase succession. Barring some kind of external catastrophe, these stands along lower Ipsut Creek will continue to be pleasingly open and spacious. Evidence of this orderly process can be seen in the much older forests at higher elevations, still further along this successional pathway.

To see and experience real "old growth" is an increasingly rare treat. There's not much left anymore. Thanks mainly to man's consumptive appetite, most old-growth forests exist now in national or state parks. The Olympic and Mount Rainier National Parks harbor the most extensive old-growth tracts in the Northwest. Some such forests are also preserved in research natural areas and in wilderness such as Glacier Peak. But virtually nothing of the Puget lowlands retains primeval character. Those forests have been converted to freeways, pastures, deciduous second growth, pole thickets of young conifers, power line rights-of-way, suburbs, and warehouses.

The harried city dweller can hustle to the mountains, there for the most part to find clearcuts, partial cuts, brushy stump lands, more second growth, real estate lots, and more commercial establishments. On both wild and managed lands, there is a bewildering variety of young forests in early successional states. If you seek real old growth outside a park, you must search diligently. As trends now appear, more and more of the remaining old-growth forests in the Cascades will be confined to reserves such as Mount Rainier National Park. Here, fortunately, they still exist.

At an elevation of around 3300 feet along the Ipsut Creek Trail, the forest assumes a rag-tag character. Avalanche paths create brushy interruptions to the forests, slicing them into patches. The trees are not so tall and many have broken tops or other deformities, especially at the higher elevations. These scars of old age give character to the large trees. So much character and individuality begins to stir resentment at the indignity of scientific nomenclature. We find ourselves before a "big specimen" and think, "What a derogatory noun! Is one's father, wife, or child a specimen?" At any rate, the largest now are Alaska yellow-cedars, western redcedar, mountain hemlock, and one gigantic noble fir.

On one of our trips to this upper basin, Miles Hemstrom recorded the vital statistics of a large mountain hemlock: 42 inches in diameter, 314 years old. Just beyond this tree loom some large Alaska yellow-cedar. The entry in Miles' notebook states simply that these are huge. One measured 91 inches at breast height diameter but could not be aged because of its rotted heartwood. What does one think upon discovering that such a magnificent tree is failing on the inside? That trees like ourselves suffer the vicissitudes of old age? That tiny, invisible organisms can claim the mightiest? Or are we more scientific and dispassionate, realizing that the processes of decay play a major role in the functioning of old-growth forest ecosystems?

There is little chance to dwell on such thoughts at this spot along the path, for beyond and somewhat upslope is a compatriot yellow-cedar nearly as large. It appears very solid. Its strippy, whitish bark is truly the garb of nobility. How old is it? Its shape and form are proud testimonials of its adaptation to this austere high-elevation environment. Here the growing season is brief; the cedar's immensity is clearly the result of centuries of growth. With blended feelings of humility, admiration, and anticipation, Miles wielded the increment corer to penetrate the secret of this tree. The tree rings were so close together that they had to be counted and recounted under high magnification. With conservative estimates added because the corer could not reach the first year ring at the heart of the massive stem, this Alaska yellow-cedar turned out to be older than any other tree measured in the park. Twelve centuries!

Foresters and the forest products industry have traditionally regarded old growth with distaste. Lands supporting such forests are perceived as wasteful and low-yielding. The stands are described as "decadent." In their view of trees as commodities, there comes a time in forest succession when rot and mortality claim many trees; when insects chew and grind away thousands of board feet of potential lumber; and when replacement stocks of healthy young trees become suppressed in the shade of the overstory. In short, they believe low-yielding old forests should be replaced by high-yielding young forests.

The concept of decadence is complemented by another powerful argument for cutting these forests down. After century upon century of nature's "investment," there accrued very large volumes of standing crop or "capital." Although some of the trees are culls because of poor form or rot, there is still plenty of merchantable wood. The great wealth of this old-growth stumpage multiplies many times when entered into the profitable chains of commerce. Consider, for example, the salaries and full employment of forest surveyors and the timber sale crew. Then contracts negotiated with the mill. Soon come the sawyers, buckers, choker-setters, and haulers. Raw materials flow into the maws of the forest products factories: sawtimber, poletimber, chips, sawdust, pulp, amber, and numerous wood chemicals. The transportation of wood and wood products unwinds along the highways, rails, and seaways. Wood products for the housing industry feed the number of "starts" each month—a basic economic indicator of the nation's health. The manufacture of consumer goods such as newspapers, toothpicks, rocking chairs, toilet paper, paint thinner, veneer, cabinets, tool handles, cardboard, telephone poles, railroad ties, violins, shakes, shingles and siding, pencils, and carved softwood bagglesnatches all conspire statistically against old growth. Some forest economists estimate that a dollar generated as stumpage on commercial forest land generates up to three times its value in the local economy. And what about all those condominiums being constructed in Las Vegas, Nevada? It is hard to estimate the multiplicative factor of the stumpage dollar in the complex web of a national economy, but estimates are as high as 40.

The dollar value of an old-growth forest in Mount Rainier National Park is staggering. Suppose such a commercial stand contains 80,000 board feet per acre of merchantable timber. Its stumpage value as high quality sawtimber is about $240 per thousand board feet. This value varies according to the composition of the trees in the stand, but can be considered as an average value of the trees sold to the highest mill bidders in 1988. About $19,000 per acre. We might assume a multiplier factor of about 20 as a compromise between the local estimate of 3 and a national estimate of 40. As the trees are harvested and the wood processed and eventually consumed as products, each acre of land has generated about $380,000 in goods and services at the national scale. A 100-acre clearcut from old growth is ultimately worth (in 1988 dollars) 38 million dollars. How many years of full employment does this represent? How many secondary businesses and industries sprout in the shadow of the forest products industries? Is it any wonder that nature's investment of centuries provides so much commercial activity in the Northwest?

The real question is, how much old growth will be left? Dollars and full employment speak loudly. To paraphrase Aldo Leopold, we can only appreciate old growth after a full breakfast. For most of us the material comforts come first, and then we turn to aesthetic and spiritual necessities. There are even some who assert that the living trees and forests are not that necessary for our inner well-being; it's only an addiction that some of us who hike or camp in the woods have come to expect. As empirical evidence, they cite the number of visits to the Grove of the Patriarchs compared to the throngs that flock to Disneyland.

To future generations, the old-growth forests of the parks will be just museum pieces, like old rugs of otherwise forgotten Oriental dynasties. Do we need these rugs? Maybe so, maybe not; but some of us view these ancient stands differently. After all, those who come to the Grove of the Patriarchs have legitimate reasons for doing so. They do not see these western redcedars as commodities. The Grove is not a timber stand. When so few old stands remain, their commercial value is no longer paramount. We seek the cultural, aesthetic, inspirational, and ecological qualities of old-growth forests and find full justification to withdraw such forests from commercial status into protected reserves. Old growth may be far more valuable than even the rarest and most precious of all those museum rugs combined. These forest stands are, as Chris Maser points out, the "parts department" for man to begin practicing long-term, sustainable forestry on this planet. To the likes of us, it is a thundering truth that this park contains much more than a giant volcano.

Just what is old-growth forest? Are these the same as virgin forests? As usual, the simplest questions are the most difficult. Our recognition depends on cultural, aesthetic, and inspirational values in part, so that precise definition becomes a matter of individual judgment. The concept of virgin forest implies something relatively untouched or unaffected by man. But this can apply to young forests, too—say 100 years after a naturally caused fire. Well, then, how about virgin forests that are old? How old is old? What characters of old forests make them old? To many, these are the forests of our frontier heritage, the wilderness stands of our ancestors, the groves encountered by Lewis and Clark, David Douglas (who unfortunately never really described them much beyond a few of the plants they contained, and whose name is memorialized by a magnificent tree species that he always referred to as a pine!), or the tough, hardy loggers of a century ago who felled these big "specimens" with hand tools. Old-growth forests are the cultural heritage in which the Pacific Northwest was settled and grew.

But old growth is more than that; it is also a feeling. It is large trees mantling a landscape unsullied by man...light filtering through spacious canopies and contributing to the moods peculiar to these majestic stands...a unique, harmonious blend of sights, sounds, and fragrances. The forests in the vicinity of Ohanapecosh Campground may be only around 250 years

Figure 39. Typical old-growth forest of Douglas-fir (right) and western hemlock (left) on the extensive Silver Fir/Alaska Huckleberry habitat type.

old, but by many they are seen as old growth. There is a certain elegance to these tall Douglas-fir and western hemlock stands along the Silver Falls Loop Trail. Perhaps in terms of forest succession, they are in the closed, pole stage, but somehow they feel like old growth.

On ecological grounds, we can do better in conceptualizing old growth. The really old forests around the Mount Rainier volcano have ecological features not found in the younger growth. Consider nitrogen cycling. In young stands of the earlier chapters, we have seen how nitrogen enters the ecosystem in association with such populations as alder or sticky laurel—plants that have nitrogen-fixing bacteria along their absorbent roots. These symbiotic plants are not important to the nitrogen cycle of old-growth forests. Instead, nitrogen enters the ecosystem by radically different routes: from nitrogen-fixing microorganisms within old, decaying logs and from blue-green algae identified with certain lichens within the tree canopies. These paths of nitrogen cycling reflect some of the structural features that help characterize old growth. In Chapter 3, we visited the world of tall canopies, where bizarre and surreal plant forms were displayed along the branches and twigs. We can now appreciate not only their light-harvesting function, but also the fact that these little plants, scattered vertically through the canopy, collectively contribute four to thirteen pounds of nitrogen per acre per year to the old-growth stand.

The most obvious feature of old growth is the big trees; trees that show the distinguishing marks of age...signs that they are in the terminal years of their natural longevity. In the Northwest, we have seen old trees with structural characteristics such as massive boles, tall canopies, dead branches, and other age deformities that distinguish them from younger trees. Tree spacing also is an important structural trait of old growth. Contrast, for example, the dense thickets and young pole stands where understories are often dark. In these young stands we often feel confined and hemmed in by the profusion of saplings, dead branches, or shrubby thickets. It's much easier to walk through most old-growth stands, especially if you don't mind using old logs as pathways.

Possibly we cannot detail all the structural complexity of an old-growth forest, but certain animals find optimum habitat in old-growth Douglas-fir-western hemlock forests. These include such birds as the northern spotted owl, pygmy owl, pileated woodpecker, saw-whet owl, goshawk, Vaux's swift, Hammond's and western flycatchers, brown creeper, hermit thrush, Townsend's and hermit warblers, pine gros-

beak, and the golden-crowned kinglet. Mammals include silver-haired and hoary bats, long-eared myotis, northern flying squirrel, and marten. The spatial arrangements of structures within old-growth forest are critical to these and other animals as a means of partitioning resources to meet their requirements of food, shelter, and reproduction. For example, the pileated woodpecker needs cavities high in the canopy for nesting, but forages among dead wood closer to the ground. The northern spotted owl seems to require a certain openness of canopy, but cannot compete with the great horned owl in younger forests where canopies are closer together.

So far, we have alluded to only one of the most important structural characteristics of old growth. Let's revisit the Carbon River Valley and look at one of those 550-year-old stands more critically. What do we see—nothing but huge trees? To the ecologist the forest is an ecosystem that contains—everything. A car stops at a pullout. Parents get out, followed by a bunch of kids needing to let off steam. "Hey, Ma, look at all the log piles!" It clicks. The child's freshness has punctured our bubble of perception, and suddenly it's so obvious. Dead wood. Decaying logs all around. Logs of ancient decay form gentle hummocks on the forest floor, coated with mosses and vascular plants. Across these are strewn more recently fallen monarchs. The dead trees still standing are referred to as snags. Large root wads mark positions from which the aged toppled. This forest is a virtual cemetery, with impressive quantities of dead wood volume and mass. Some big stems are stacked on top of others, forming bridges along which the youngsters scamper with delight, eight or ten feet above the ground.

Of course, younger stands contain dead wood, too. Witness the slash after a logging operation or the strewn residues in an avalanche track. The self-thinning of dense pole stands brings about numerous snags and down saplings or poles. But an old-growth stand will contain logs in all stages of decay, culminating in advanced decomposition and their gradual disappearance. Biologists studying the decay of Douglas-fir logs developed a system for identifying five decay stages, which are summarized in Table 2. Each decay class represents a state of biological succession, a condition in which the log is host for a complex microcosm of specific organisms. The multitudinous populations involved in these food web activities in coarse woody debris are another characteristic of old-growth forest. Down logs are essential microhabitats for birds, mammals, reptiles, and amphibians that use them for lookout and feeding sites, cover, food foraging and storage, or bedding and

Table 2. A five-class scheme for rating stages of decomposition in Douglas-fir logs.

CHARACTERISTIC			DECAY CLASS		
	1	2	3	4	5
Bark	intact	mostly intact	partly intact to sloughing	absent	absent
Specific Gravity	0.45	0.42	0.36	0.26	0.05
Exposed Wood	intact	intact to partly soft	large, hard pieces	small, soft, blocky pieces	soft and powdery (when dry)
Epiphytes	none	mosses	mosses, conifer seedlings (small)	shrubs, tree seedlings & saplings	shrubs, tree seedl. & saplings
Invading Roots	none	none	conifer seedlings	in sapwood only	in sapwood & heartwood
Mycorrhizae	none	none	none	in sapwood	in sapwood & heartwood
Portion of Log on the Ground	support points	support points, slightly sagging	log is sagging	all	all
Fungal Fruiting Bodies (selected)	none	Cyathus Tremella Fomitopsis Polyporus	Polyporellus Mycena Marasmius	Cortinarius Collybia Cantharellus	

reproduction.

What mystery lurks under a log? Remember how, as kids, we loved to roll them over in search of salamanders, grubs, white ants, bizarre beetles, spiders, giant centipedes or millipedes, slugs, or furry rodents? Every log was a different entry to the hidden, dark, moist, punky world. We can't roll these monsters over, but the same hidden universe is present below and within.

Even as a tree dies (decay class 1), it already contains hosts of organisms important to its decomposition. For let us realize at the onset that decay is a living process, the consequence of metabolism of those feeding upon the tree and those feeding upon the feeders, and so forth along the food web. The erect new snag or fresh-fallen tree is being worked on by chewers, shredders, and grinders; these are mostly wood-feeding insects tunneling into heartwood or sapwood or, in some cases, specializing upon the phloem or bark tissue. The guts of these feeders contain microorganisms capable of digesting the woody diet.

As the wood of these tunnels and cavities or on the outer parts of the bole becomes exposed to moisture or wetting-drying cycles, it is soon penetrated by germinating hyphae from spores of wood decay fungi. These fungi grow on the moist wood, converting the chemical compounds of the substrate into living hyphae and making use of the chemical energy of wood compounds to drive the process. Different fungi are capable of breaking down different wood chemicals—starches, resins, lignin, cellulose, and hemicellulose. As the fungal biomass within the log increases, other groups of organisms appear: fungivorous mites, nematodes, collembolans, and bacteria. And then still others, the predators upon these wood or fungus eaters: arachnids, centipedes, salamanders, woodpeckers, winter wrens, and others.

And so the organic processes continue. By stage 2, the wood decay fungi begin fruiting. We can

Figure 40. Beds of rotten logs in an old-growth forest serve as nurseries for mosses and other plants; the tree has as many ecological functions to fulfill after it dies as when it is alive.

see the bracket mushrooms and fruiting structures of various gilled, pore, and toothed fungi on logs and snags. The log riddled with feeding organisms has lost some of its rigidity so that it sags between its support points. Partly decayed soft spots mark the ever deeper penetration of fungal or bacterial populations into the heartwood.

Sometime during stage 3, nitrogen-fixing bacteria appear within the log. Wood tissue is notoriously low in nitrogen; what little there is has by now been transferred to the living biomass of other log organisms. These bacteria obtain their supply by converting inorganic atmospheric nitrogen into organic nitrogen. In certain old-growth forests, scientists have estimated that the nitrogen fixed in logs amounts to about 170 pounds per acre. At present, the rates of fixation and the availability of this organic nitrogen to other organisms are less known, but it seems clear that

old logs are a major avenue of nitrogen entry in old-growth ecosystems.

About the time organic nitrogen becomes fixed in decaying logs, hemlocks appear upon them as established seedlings. In stages 3 and 4, the log has become a fertile, organic rooting medium. Mycorrhizal symbiosis, which we encountered in Chapter 3, is now well developed even in the deeper parts of the log. The "nurse log" is decked with a lush vegetation of young trees, huckleberries, salal, ferns, grasses, and mosses. The woody matrix of the log gradually disappears as centuries elapse. Generations of rodents, scurrying under the shelter of the log or occupying the hollow recesses within, have inoculated the log with spores of new wood decay fungi and ensured their growth by manuring with urine and feces.

We break off a soft chunk of wood and notice panicky cryptozoans hastening into the moist, dark

Figure 41. Wood decay fungi fruiting on a western hemlock tree that died recently.

Figure 42. Large Douglas-fir in class 3 decay stage; it has just begun to serve as a nurse log and is sloughing much of its bark.

interior. Many detritus animals cannot be seen without a hand lens—assorted mites, collembolans, or nematodes. The log has long since collapsed on the ground and is noticeably flattened. A gelatinous bright orange or yellow growth is sometimes found—the sexual and fruiting stages of slime molds—striking evidence that microbial wood decay activities are still going on and will continue until the log disappears altogether, somewhere around four to six centuries after tree death, by some estimates, or about nine centuries by other calculations.

Were the old foresters correct, then, in describing old growth as decadent...that rot was eating away the vitality of the forest ecosystem...that the whole production process was slowing down or becoming negative...and "waste" was rampant? The detrital processes as described above operate to cause wood to disappear and to reduce the quantity of wood

in a stand. These are essentially respiratory processes because they concern the metabolism of non-green organisms organized into complex detrital food webs. The respiratory burden of young growth is less because its decay systems are less complex, the amount of coarse woody debris is less, and the time factor of mortality and buildup of wood residues in each of the five decay stages is shorter. However, to properly compare young and old-growth forests, we must also look at the other side of the coin—the side that reflects production processes. The most important of these is the primary production process, for this results in the buildup and accumulation of plant biomass, principally wood, within the stand. It is the balance between buildup and disappearance, or primary production versus respiratory processes, that distinguishes old growth from young or intermediate growth and presents the forester with the measure of net forest productivity.

As we view the great logs and huge trees of this Carbon River old growth, we reflect upon the analogy of some big machine, some kind of piston with a work stroke and an exhaust stroke. Sunlight, of course, is the power source. Filtering through all that greenery, tier after tier of foliage from the canopy top to the mossy surfaces of logs, the sun's electromagnetic radiation is the fuel of forest ecosystems. The structural apparatus for the power stroke is impressive here: every square yard of forest floor area is canopied, on the average, by about forty square yards of green leaf surface. Chlorophyll, the critical substance of our fantastic machine, is displayed in billions of leafy arrangements within this voluminous old-growth space. The cholorphyll itself is mostly structured in very orderly arrangements within the chloroplasts of leaf tissue, and here the very basic work function of the machine takes place as inorganic carbon dioxide and water are combined into high energy plant sugars. The power stroke...an infinity of power strokes, each with an infinitesimal contribution to the forest whole.

If we look upon trees as commodities, the sunlight powers the chemical bonding energy that is basic to wood production; if we view this forest as an ecosystem, the sunlight drives the entire trophic structure—all the populations of plants, animals, and microorganisms feeding upon one another.

The remainder of our giant forest, which includes all living things except green tissue—the stems and branches of trees and shrubs, all the fauna, the microorganisms, the cryptozoan residents of the snags, logs, and litter mats, and the most humble of slime molds—are components of the intricately structured exhaust stroke of this ecosystem. The energy source of these organisms commences with the chemical-bonding energy of plant tissue, which is converted along myriad organic pathways to other forms of biochemical energy and ultimately to carbon dioxide, water, and simple mineral molecules. An infinity of exhaust strokes, most of which occur (in organisms higher on the evolutionary scale) in tissues where microscopic structures called mitochondria are located. The sum contribution of these infinitesimal exhaust strokes in the whole forest is the loss of organic matter and the dissipation of chemical energy as heat.

Ecologists combine the power and exhaust strokes into formulations of energy flux and biogeochemical cycles of carbon, oxygen, and mineral elements, such as nitrogen or phosphorus. The old-growth forest ecosystem is vastly more complicated than anything man-made. We can marvel at the spectacular gross structure of the forest here at Carbon River or elsewhere, but this marvel still contains numerous unseen or unstudied components of which little is known. Questions abound. What are the chemical attractants or repellants of the "who eats whom" or "who eats what" inside a rotting log? What causes the aging process of cells that first invites parasitism and then death? Why are there so many different kinds of tiny mites in the ferments of coniferous humus? Why are the western redcedars and Alaska yellow-cedars so often rotted at the center, when they are used to make shakes or shingles because of their relative resistance to rot, while trees like Douglas-fir are usually free of heartwood rot in many stands?

Let's return to the primary productivity of an old-growth forest. Until recently, little attention was given to the subject of "yield" in truly old forests. The general assumption was that this measure would be low since so much of the forest "crop" consisted of massive organs such as stems, branches, and roots , which by themselves consume photosynthetic products with little left over for wood production. Measurements of the primary productivity of old growth, mostly coniferous stands in Oregon, found that the production of photosynthetic sugars and their derivatives (e.g., wood) was comparable to that found in younger forests. The coniferous foliage measured on the order of 4.5 to 9.0 tons per acre in 450-year-old stands and was similar in magnitude to fully stocked stands 90 to 130 years old. However, a substantial part of foliage biomass in old growth was found to be in the form of shade-tolerant trees such as hemlocks or true firs. Nevertheless, the fact remains that the conversion of energy from sunlight to plant tissue is as efficient in old-growth forests as it is in young stands.

The respiration cost of old-growth forest is also high. To maintain living tissue requires an increasing tax upon the gross photosynthetic yield as the amount of non-green tree biomass increases with age. And when a tree dies, photosynthesis ceases; but respiration continues as decay, with a net result of biomass loss, or negative production. Net production in a forest stand is the difference between gross primary production (the cumulative power strokes) and stand respiration; this is mostly seen as the quantity of wood added or lost in the stand.

One old-growth Douglas-fir-western hemlock forest in the western Washington Cascades produced about 106 cubic feet of wood per acre per year over a 12-year period. Its net production was slightly positive—more wood added than lost. In the long run, the living biomass of old-growth stands seems to fluctuate around a plateau according to episodes of heavy or light mortality. For example, if beetle epidemics or unusual windthrow cause high mortality in old trees, the loss of living wood may exceed gross production. This period might be followed by an era of net positive productivity as the foliage of released understory trees again fills up the spaces vacated by mortality.

Regardless of the spatial dynamics of mortality and growth that maintains living tree volume around some plateau, an old-growth forest continues to accumulate total biomass. This buildup is mostly in the form of snags and logs. At present there are few good measures concerning how long the decay stages of Table 2 last, especially in the climates of Mount Rainier and in logs other than Douglas-fir. Tentative indications show that in forests 300 to about 700 years old the coarse woody debris still is accumulating, i.e., logs and snags of various decay stages are added more

rapidly than they can be decomposed. But few measurements have been taken in thousand-year-old stands, such as those along Chinook Creek, where the total biomass amounts have possibly peaked.

Now that our eyes are attuned to the snags and logs around us, it is apparent that the totality of dead plus living volume or woody mass is impressive. This total at Mount Rainier and at a few other locations in the Northwest, including the redwood stands of California, exceeds any other softwood forest in the world. The mountain ash (*Eucalyptus regnans*) forests in Australia also are tall and voluminous and are probably the most massive hardwood stands of the temperate regions. But our old-growth stands in the Northwest have no equals among the world's softwood forests. In sheer size and volume, they are, quite simply, stupendous.

As we have noted, old-growth forests can be characterized in part by the existence of trees nearing

Figure 43. Typically 20 percent of the biomass in old-growth forests is in snags and downed logs; large snags, such as the one shown here, are critically important habitat for all types of animals.

102

the terminal years of their natural longevity. At some
of the higher elevations of Mount Rainier, such as
upper Laughingwater Creek, Cataract Creek, and
Kotsuck Creek, the forests may be so ancient that most
of the long-lived seral trees have died out. We know
that Alaska yellow-cedar can persist for over a
millenium and in some situations can be a minor tree
of climax forests. But what happens when even this
droopy, resilient tree of cold, snowy forests is no
longer regenerating and the last of the old trees finally
joins the assemblage of decaying logs on the forest
floor? Then the forest tree populations, from seedlings
to the very aged, are almost pure forests of silver fir.

Interestingly, this climax fir does not have
very impressive longevity: the maximum ages are
about 600 years, but most of the old trees die when
they become 400 to 500 years old. Climax stands of
single-species purity are rare in the park, but they do
exist. Perhaps an occasional mountain hemlock will
obstinately punctuate this canopy of conical silver fir
crowns, for the hemlock is also able to germinate and
grow in the shaded and snow-filled interiors of seral
and late seral high elevation forests. Sometimes these
big mountain hemlocks will exhibit stilt roots—the
logs that they germinated on have completely disappeared. But the sporadic hemlock serves only to
emphasize the nearly complete takeover of the forest
by silver fir. We can't know how old these pure silver
fir forests really are because, as mentioned, the oldest
individual trees are less than 600 years old. Perhaps
one, two, or a half dozen generations of fir have come
and gone. Perhaps all the decay stages of logs consist
of silver fir; or maybe decay classes 4 and 5 also
contain some Douglas-fir or noble fir.

I recall one sunny August day when some of
us were hiking to Spray Park. As we passed Spray
Falls, Jerry Franklin, who can sense old growth by
some kind of mystic vibration, called our attention to
some large, rounded crowns on a distant ridge.
"There's a good stand—you might look for a plot to
take measurements," he advised as we continued our
way to Spray Park. Since Jerry had not been in these
Mowich drainages before, I wondered how he could be
so sure. On our return later in the day, the rest of us
braved life and limb crossing Spray Creek below the
falls and headed toward the indicated ridge. Jerry
didn't come; he had to get back to camp. But he knew
what we would find. A half hour of scrambling
brought us into the stand. The late afternoon's low-
angle light suffused the forest interior in rich color.
The forest floor was a luscious green, like the richest,
freshest meadows I could possibly imagine. This was
my favorite kind of forest, the SILVER FIR/

FOAMFLOWER type, carpeted with soft ferns,
valerians, foamflowers, and dozens more. The trees
were widely spaced and allowed the light to bathe the
ground and its silvery stems—those tall, incredibly
straight, lichen-covered stems, all of silver fir. A
forest of the purest purity.

It's possible that there might once have been
some noble fir here, so I looked around at the logs,
which can be identified in decay stages 1-3 by persisting remnants of the purple, platy bark. Well, if it was
ever here, the last of them had long since died, at least
to decay stage 4 or beyond, however many centuries
that takes.

Remember, the seeds of noble fir, as well as
Alaska yellow-cedar, mountain hemlock, subalpine fir,
and maybe even Douglas-fir, are periodically raining
into this stand from seed trees at other locations.
Those seeds are testing, continually sampling environmental conditions here to see if their time has arrived,
a time to trigger a different kind of forest. But no—
not yet, not this year. Try again next year, or the year
after. For now the silver fir reigns absolute. The chain
of replacement of one silver fir generation by the next
has endless links. Only an act of God can break those
links (or, more scientifically, some kind of external
catastrophe), but we know that even this will happen
sooner or later. We can sense the foreboding nearness
of those upper, ice-crunched, restless slopes of the
volcano's summit. The evening tranquility of this
climax stand is as transient as a sheet of water rolling
off the lip of Spray Falls. But for a thousand years
silver fir had awaited this day, and the day is theirs.
As I wandered around this stand in the fading light, I
reflected upon the coincidence of my own transience
with this moment of the silver fir's glory. It was truly
a moment to be savored.

We returned to camp by starlight.

Suggested Further Reading

General

Crandell, Dwight R. 1969. The geologic story of Mount Rainier. Geol. Survey Bul. 1292, 43 p.

Franklin, Jerry F. and C.T. Dyrness. 1973. Natural vegetation of Oregon and Washington. U.S.D.A. Forest Service Gen. Tech. Rep. PNW-8, viii, 417 p.

Hitchcock, C. Leo and Arthur Cronquist. 1973. *Flora of the Pacific Northwest.* Univ. Washington Press, Seattle, xix, 730 p.

Jones, George Neville. 1938. The flowering plants and ferns of Mount Rainier. Univ. Wash. Publ. Biol. 7, 192 p., 9 plates, Univ. Washington Press, Seattle.

Kirk, Ruth. 1968. *Exploring Mount Rainier.* Univ. Washington Press, Seattle, 104 p.

Ramaley, F. 1916. Dry grassland of a high mountain park in northern Colorado. Plant World 19:249-270.

Schofield, W.B. 1969. *Some Mosses of British Columbia.* British Columbia Provincial Museum Handbook 28, 262 p.

Chapters 1 & 2

Brockway, Dale G., Christopher Topik, Miles A. Hemstrom, and William H. Emmingham. 1983. Plant association and management guide for the Pacific silver fir zone, Gifford Pinchot National Forest. U.S.D.A. Forest Service Pacific Northwest Region, R6-Ecol-130a-1983, iii, 122 p., Portland, OR.

Franklin, Jerry F., William H. Moir, Miles A. Hemstrom, Sarah E. Greene, and Bradley E. Smith. 1988. The forest communities of Mount Rainier National Park, National Park Service Scientific Monograph Series 19, xvi, 194 p +2 color maps, U.S. Gov. Printing Office, Washington, D.C.

Zobel, Donald B., Arthur McKee, Glenn M. Hawk, and C.T. Dyrness. 1976. Relationships of environment to composition, structure, and diversity of forest communities of the central western Cascades of Oregon. Ecol. Monographs 46: 135-156.

Chapter 3

Bates, Marston. 1960. *The Forest and the Sea.* The New American Library (Mentor Books), New York, NY, 216 p.

Evans, Howard Ensign. 1966. *Life on a Little Known Planet.* Dell Publishing Co., 318 p.

Furman, Thomas E. and James M. Trappe. 1971. Phylogeny and ecology of mycotrophic achlorophyllous angiosperms. Quart. Rev. Biology 46: 219-225.

Hobson, F.D. 1976. Classification system for the soils of Mount Rainier National Park. M.S. Thesis, Washington State Univ., 79 p., Pullman, WA.

Mullineaux, D.R. 1974. Pumice and other pyroclastic deposits in Mount Rainier National Park, Washington. Geol. Surv. Bul. 1326, viii, 83 p.

_____ and D.R. Crandell. 1981. The eruptive history of Mount St. Helens. U.S. Geol. Survey Professional Paper 1250: 3-15.

Pike, L.H., W.C. Denison, D.M. Tracy, M.A. Sherwood, and F.M. Roades. 1975. Floristic survey of epiphytic lichens and bryophytes growing on old-growth conifers in western Oregon. The Bryologist 75: 389-402.

Waring, R.H. and J.F. Franklin. 1979. The evergreen coniferous forests of the Pacific Northwest. Science 204: 1380-1386.

Chapters 4 & 5

Fraser, Don Lee. 1983. Yacolt regreened. From ashes to answers: the great Northwest fires. American Forests 89(8).

Hemstrom, Miles A. and Jerry F. Franklin. 1982. Fire and other disturbances of the forests in Mount Rainier National Park. Quaternary Res. 18: 32-51.

Holbrook, Steward H. 1943. *Burning an Empire. The Story of American Forest Fires.* The MacMillan Co., New York, xiv, 229 p.

Morris, William G. 1934. Forest fires in western Oregon and western Washington. Oregon Hist. Quart. 35: 313-339.

Plummer, F.G. 1899. Mount Rainier Forest Reserve, Washington. U.S. Dept. Interior Geological Survey 21st Report 1900 (1902), Part 5, pp 81-143.

Chapter 6

Clark, Ella E. 1953. *Indian Legends of the Pacific Northwest*. Univ. California Press, Berkeley, CA.

Crandell, Dwight R. 1971. Postglacial lahars from Mount Rainier volcano, Washington. U.S. Geol. Survey Professional Paper 677, 75 p + maps.

Frenzen, Peter M., Marianne E. Krasny, and Lisa P. Rigney. 1988. Thirty-three years of plant succession on the Kautz Creek mudflow, Mount Rainier National Park, Washington. Canadian J. Botany 66:130-137.

Maser, Chris, and Zane Maser. 1988. Interactions among squirrels, mycorrhizal fungi, and coniferous forests in Oregon. Great Basin Naturalist 48:358-369.

Trappe, J.M., J.F. Franklin, R.F. Tarrant, and G.M. Hensen (Eds.). 1968. Biology of alder. Pacific Northwest For. & Range Expt. Station, iv, 292 p, Portland, OR.

Chapter 7

Armstrong, J.E., D.R. Crandell, D.J. Easterbrook, and J.B. Noble. 1965. Late Pleistocene stratigraphy and chronology in southeastern British Columbia and northwestern Washington. Geol. Soc. Amer. Bul. 76: 321-330.

Bryson, Reid A. and Thomas J. Murray. 1977. *Climates of Hunger. Mankind and the World's Changing Weather*. Univ. Wisconsin Press, Madison, xv, 171 p.

Crandell, D.R. 1969. Surficial geology of Mount Rainier National Park, Washington. U.S. Geological Survey Bul. 1288.

_____ and R.D. Miller. 1964. Post-hypsithermal glacier advances at Mount Rainier, Washington. U.S. Geological Survey Professional Paper 501-D: D110-D-114.

Franklin, J.F., W.H. Moir, G.W. Douglas, and C. Wiberg. 1971. Invasion of subalpine meadows by trees in the Cascade Range, Washington and Oregon. Arctic & Alpine Res. 3: 215-224.

Hansen, H.P. 1947. Postglacial forest succession, climate, and chronology in the Pacific Northwest. Amer. Philos. Soc. Trans. 37: 1-130.

Heusser, Calvin J. 1965. A Pleistocene phytogeographical sketch of the Pacific Northwest and Alaska. pp 469-483 IN: H.E. Wright, Jr. and David E. Frey (Eds.) The Quaternary of the United States, Princeton Univ. Press, Princeton, NJ, x, 922 p.

Ladurie, E.L. 1971. *Times of Feast, Times of Famine: A History of Climate Since the Year 1000*. Translated by Barbara Bray. Doubleday, New York.

Löve, Doris. 1970. Subarctic and subalpine: where and what? Arctic & Alpine Res. 2: 63-73.

Richardson, Donald. 1968. Glacial outburst floods in the Pacific Northwest. U.S. Geol. Survey Professional Paper 600-D: D79-D86.

Sigafoos, Robert S. and E.L.Hendricks. 1972. Recent activity of glaciers of Mount Rainier, Washington. U.S. Geol. Survey Professional Paper 387-B, 24 p.

Stuiver, Minze, Calvin J. Heusser, and In Che Yang. 1978. North American glacial history extended 75,000 years ago. Science 200: 16-21.

Chapter 8

Franklin, Jerry F., Kermit Cromack, Jr., William Denison, Arthur McKee, Chris Maser, James Sedell, Fred Swanson, and Glen Juday. 1981. Ecological characteristics of old-growth Douglas-fir forests. U.S.D.A. Forest Serv. Gen. Tech. Rep. PNW-118, 48 p.

Harmon, M.E., J.F. Franklin, *et al*, 1986. Ecology of coarse woody debris in temperate ecosystems. Adv. Ecol. Res. 15: 133-302.

Harris, Larry D. 1984. *The Fragmented Forest. Island Biogeographic Theory and the Preservation of Biotic Diversity*. Univ. Chicago Press, Chicago and London, xviii, 211 p.

Society of American Foresters. 1984. Scheduling the
harvest of old growth. Soc. Amer. Foresters, 5400
Grosvenor Lane, Bethesda, MD, 20814, 44 p.

Maser, Chris. 1988. *The Redesigned Forest.* R & E
Miles, San Pedro CA, xx, 236 p.

_____, James M. Trappe, and Ronald A. Nussbaum.
1978. Fungal-small mammal interrelationships with
emphasis on Oregon coniferous forests. Ecology 59:
799-808.

_____ and J.M. Trappe, Technical Editors. 1984.
The seen and unseen world of the fallen tree.
U.S.D.A. Forest Serv. Gen. Tech. Rep. PNW-164,
Pacific Northwest Forest & Range Exp. Station,
Portland, OR. 56 p.

_____, Robert F. Tarrant, James M. Trappe, and Jerry
F. Franklin, Technical Editors. 1988. From the Forest
to the Sea: A Story of Fallen Trees. U.S.D.A. Forest
Service Gen. Tech. Rep. PNW-GTR-229, Pacific
Northwest Res. Station and U.S.D.I. Bureau Land
Management, Portland, OR, 153 p.

106

Technical Glossary

Alluvium   Soil or rock material carried and deposited primarily by water. Cf colluvium.

Andesite   The principal lava (or molten rock) that flowed from eruptions of Mount Rainier. Andesite is characterized by its mineral composition intermediate between granite-rhyolite and gabbro-basalt.

Ash   Mineral material falling from the sky after a volcanic eruption. Syn. volcanic ash, tephra.

Autotrophic   Literally "self nutrition," refers to a green plant's ability to manufacture carbohydrates from water and atmospheric carbon dioxide through the process of photosynthesis. Cf mycotrophic.

Bench   A landform characterized by a gentle slope bounded above and below by steeper slopes. Benches are often formed by slumping (or mass wasting) of deep, saturated soils on steep mountain slopes.

Biomass   The mass of living or dead tissue, usually expressed as an oven or air dry weight; for example, the biomass of a log.

Canopy   The above-ground mass of trees or shrubs, especially the branches and twigs together with the leaves they bear.

Cirque   A rounded valley basin carved by a glacier.

Colluvium   Soil or rock material deposited downslope primarily by the combined action of gravity and water. Cf alluvium.

Cryptozoan   Literally "hidden animals." Small, inconspicuous animals such as mites, protozoans, collembolans, or other invertebrates which form complex food webs in the soil or litter of the forest floor.

Dbh   See Diameter at breast height.

Detritus   Organic debris consisting of dead cells and tissues, mostly of plant parts. Syn. litter; adj. detrital.

Diameter at breast height   A tree's stem diameter at 55 inches from the ground as measured by a diameter tape which converts circumference (C) to diameter(d) using the equation C= πd.

Drift   The rubble, mostly of mineral material, deposited by melting glaciers.

Ecosystem   The machinery of nature which involves all the dependencies and relationships of organisms and their environment.

Ecotone   A sharp or gradual boundary between one plant community and another in the landscape. If the boundary is very abrupt, it is sometimes called an edge.

Epiphyte   A plant, either parasitic or free-living, which grows upon another plant.

Even-aged   A forest stand whose trees germinated or were planted within a relatively short period of time. Even-aged stands at Mount Rainier have about 80 percent of the trees becoming established in about a 50-year interval after forest clearing.

Fire line   A rather abrupt boundary between forests of different composition, age, or structure as the result of a fire. Cf ecotone.

Horizon   A morphologically distinctive layer of the soil, as for example, an illuvial horizon.

Hypha (plural hyphae)   One of the tubular filaments comprising the living tissue of a fungus.

Hypsithermal   A period of high temperatures in the Pacific Northwest from about 10,800 to about 3,500 years ago. Elsewhere in North America this warming period has been called the altithermal.

Illuvial   A soil layer in which material from an overlying layer has been precipitated from solution or deposited from suspension.

Interstade   A climatic interval of global warming, often measured in centuries, characterized by receding glaciers and residual ice masses of restricted size and mass. Also, interstadia.

Invertebrate Animals without backbones, such as insects, snails, worms, spiders, mites, or nematodes.

Iron pan A hard and water-impermeable layer of soil caused by cementation of soil particles by precipitates of iron minerals.

Meadow Dense herbaceous plant communities occurring in relatively moist environments in an otherwise forested region. Sometimes low shrubs also occur among the herbs. Meadow is a generic term that includes but is not limited to temporary communities that will return to forests in the process of succession. Cf park, parkland, subalpine meadow.

Microhabitat A small locale (such as a gully) or site (such as a fallen log) that has its own particular environmental features such as temperature, moisture, humidity, biota, etc.

Mycorrhizae An association of fungal cells and the cells of root systems of vascular plants in direct contact and exchanging food and minerals.

Mycotrophic Literally "fungus nutrition." Refers to vascular plants that have become partially or completely dependent upon soil fungi for their nutrition.

Overstory The uppermost canopy of vegetation when viewed from above. Opp. understory.

Park A natural meadow opening in an otherwise forested landscape.

Parkland A landscape in which forests and meadows form mosaics. An example is Yakima Park, where small groves of trees form islands in natural subalpine grassland.

Periglacial Adjective referring to climates or environments in the more or less immediate vicinity of large continental or alpine ice masses.

Phloem The food-conducting tissue of a vascular plant. Cf xylem.

Plot A small area within the forest stand used as a measured sample of the stand as a whole.

Pole A tree with a stem diameter at breast height between 9 and 16 inches. Cf seedling, sapling.

Raceme A pattern of individual, stalked flowers arranged along a single main stem of a plant.

Rhizome Horizontal underground stems of a vascular plant.

Regeneration In forestry terminology, regeneration refers to the tree seedlings, saplings, or even smaller poles, often in the understory, many of which will survive to become the next generation of dominant trees.

Root crown A rather vague region of an individual tree between the base of the trunk and the place of branching of the major roots.

Sapling Young or small trees with stem diameters at breast height between 2 and 9 inches. Cf seedling, pole.

Scarp An abrupt and often steep change of slope between one geological feature and another. For example, a fault scarp.

Seedling Established young or small trees with stem diameters less than 2 inches at breast height. Cf sapling, pole.

Serac A pinnacle of ice among the crevasses of a glacier.

Snowpack The accumulation of snow persisting from one storm to another and attaining various depths and densities according to melting and freezing weather conditions.

Stade A climatic episode of global cooling in which glaciers advance, cover large areas, and attain large masses. Also stadia. Cf interstade.

Subalpine A vegetation zone between the upper altitudinal tree line and the lower, closed-canopy, more or less continuous coniferous forest.

Subalpine meadow Herb- or low-shrub-dominated communities in the subalpine. Some common herbs at Mount Rainier include lupines, valerian, meadow fleabane, fan-leaf cinquefoil, and green fescue. Some common low shrubs are mountain heath and blue-leafed huckleberry. Cf meadow, park.

Succession An orderly and usually predictable process in which a plant community is gradually replaced by another plant community.

108

Symbiotic   Any two or more species of organisms living in direct contact and interdependency. For example, the cellulose-decomposing micro-organisms in the intestines of wood-eating termites.

Talus   Fragments of rock and other soil material accumulated by gravity at the foot of cliffs, steep slopes, or steep snow fields. The latter is often referred to at Mount Rainier as protalus ramparts.

Tephra   See ash.

Trophic   Relationship of one organism to another in the food chain, often expressed as "who eats whom" or "who nourishes whom."

Understory   Any individual plant or portion of one occurring below the vertical projection of another plant. Opp. overstory.

Vascular plant   A plant having specialized and well developed tissues for conducting food and water. Includes all the flowering plants and the conspicuous ferns, i.e., their sporophyte generation. Nonvascular plants include fungi, mosses, and liverworts.

Vertebrate   An animal with backbones. Vertebrates include mammals, birds, fish, reptiles, and amphibians. Opp. invertebrate.

Xylem   Water-conducting tissues of plants. Xylem comprises the main subsistance of wood. Heartwood is mostly dead tissue, while sapwood is the living tissue of a tree stem. Cf phloem.

Glossary of Botanical and Common Names

(Nomenclature follows Hitchcock and Cronquist 1973)

Trees

Alaska cedar	
Alaska yellow-cedar	*Chamaecyparis nootkatensis* (D. Don) Spach
Alder	*Alnus* Hill
Big leaf maple	*Acer macrophyllum* Pursh
Black cottonwood	*Populus trichocarpa* T & G
Douglas-fir	*Pseudotsuga menziesii* (Mirbel) Franco var. *menziesii*
Douglas maple	*Acer glabrum* Torr. var. *douglasii* (Hook) Dippel
Engelmann spruce	*Picea engelmannii* Parry
Grand fir	*Abies grandis* (Dougl.) Forbes
Lodgepole pine	*Pinus contorta* Dougl.
Mountain hemlock	*Tsuga mertensiana* (Bong.) Carr.
Noble fir	*Abies procera* Rehder
Ponderosa pine	*Pinus ponderosa* Laws.
Red alder	*Alnus rubra* Bong.
Silver fir	*Abies amabilis* (Dougl.) Forbes
Sitka alder	*Alnus sinuata* (Regel) Rydb.
Sitka spruce	*Picea sitchensis* (Bong.) Carr.
Subalpine fir	*Abies lasiocarpa* (Hook.) Nutt.
Western hemlock	*Tsuga heterophylla* (Raf.) Sarg.
Western redcedar	*Thuja plicata* Donn
Western white pine	*Pinus monticola* Dougl.
White bark pine	*Pinus albicaulis* Engelm.
Yew	*Taxus brevifolia* Nutt.

Shrubs and Herbs

Alaska huckleberry	*Vaccinium alaskaense* Howell
Alum root	*Heuchera* L.
Arnica	*Arnica* L.
Avalanche fawnlily	*Erythronium montanum* Wats.
Beadlily	*Clintonia uniflora* (Schult.) Kunth
Bearberry	*Arctostaphylos uva-ursi* (L.)Spreng.
Beargrass	*Xerophyllum tenax* (Pursh) Nutt.
Bedstraw	*Galium* L.
Bent grass	*Agrostis* L.
Betony	*Stachys cooleyi* Heller
Big huckleberry	*Vaccinium membranaceum* Dougl.
Big-leaf huckleberry	*V. membranaceum* Dougl.
Black huckleberry	*V. membranaceum* Dougl.
Bracken fern	*Pteridium aquilinum* (L.) Kuhn.
Broadleaved montia	*Montia cordifolia* (Wats.) Pax &Hoffm.
Bunchberry	*Cornus canadensis* L.
Candystick	*Allotropa virgata* T. & G.
Cinquefoil	*Potentilla* L.
Coral root	*Corallorhiza* Chat.
Current	*Ribes* L.
Deer fern	*Blechnum spicant* (L.) With.
Devil's club	*Oplopanax horridum* (Smith) Miq.
Dewberry	*Rubus ursinus* Cham. & Schlecht.
Douglas maple	*Acer glabrum* Torr. var *douglasii* (Hook.) Dippel
Dwarf bramble	*Rubus lasiococcus* Gray
Elderberry	*Sambucus* L.
Enchanter's nightshade	*Circaea alpina* L.
Evergreen violet	*Viola sempervirens* Greene
False solomon seal	*Smilacina* Desf.
Fan-leaf cinquefoil	*Potentilla flabellifolia* Hook.
Fawnlily	*Erythronium* L.
Fireweed	*Epilobium angustifolium* L.
Fleabane	*Erigeron* L.
Foamflower	*Tiarella* L.
Fool's huckleberry	*Menziesia ferruginea* Smith
Fragile fern	*Cystopteris fragilis* (L.) Bernh.
Fragrant bedstraw	*Galium triflorum* Michx.
Gayophytum	*Gayophytum* Juss.
Geyer sedge	*Carex geyeri* Boott.
Gnome plant	*Hemitomes congestum* Gray
Green fescue	*Festuca viridula* Vasey
Hazelnut	*Corylus cornuta* Marsh.
Heather	*Phyllodoce* Salisb. and *Cassiope* D.Don
Huckleberry	*Vaccinium* L.
Indian pipe	*Monotropa uniflora* L.
Kinnikinnick	*Arctostaphylos uva-ursi* (L.)Spreng.
Lady fern	*Athyrium filix-femina* (L.) Roth.
Leafy lousewort	*Pedicularis racemosa* Dougl.
Licorice fern	*Polypodium glycyrrhiza* D.C. Eat.
Lupine	*Lupinus* L. especially L. *latifolius* Agardh.
Manzanita	*Arctostaphylos* Adans.
Meadow fleabane	*Erigeron peregrinus* (Pursh) Greene
Mistletoe	*Loranthaceae*
Mitrewort	*Mitella* L.
Oak fern	*Gymnocarpium dryopteris* (L.) Newm.
One-sided wintergreen	*Pyrola secunda* L.
Orchids	*Orchidaceae*

110

Oregon grape	*Berberis nervosa* Pursh
Oregon wood sorrel	*Oxalis oregana* Nutt.
Oval-leaf huckleberry	*Vaccinium ovalifolium* Smith
Paintbrush	*Castilleja Mutis* ex L.f.
Pearly everlasting	*Anaphalis margaritacea* (L.) B & H
Phantom orchid	*Eburophyton austiniae* (Gray) Heller
Pinedrops	*Pterospora andromedea* Nutt.
Pine sap	*Hypopitys monotropa* Crantz.
Pipsissewa	*Chimaphila* Pursh
Rattlesnake plantain	*Goodyeara oblongifolia* Raf.
Red huckleberry	*Vaccinium parvifolium* Smith
Rhododendron	*Rhododendron albiflorum* Hook.
Ross sedge	*Carex rossii* Boott.
Rusty leaf	*Menziesia ferruginea* Smith
Salal	*Gaultheria shallon* Pursh
Salmonberry	*Rubus spectabilis* Pursh
Scouler's corydalis	*Corydalis scouleri* Hook.
Scouler's willow	*Salix scouleriana* Barratt.
Sedges	*Cyperaceae* and *Carex* L.
Serviceberry	*Amelanchier alnifolia* Nutt.
Silvergreen	*Adenocaulon bicolor* Hook.
Sitka alder	*Alnus sinuata* (Regel) Rydb.
Skunk cabbage	*Lysichitum americanum* Hulten & St.John.
Small wintergreen	*Pyrola picta* Smith
Spotted catsear	*Hypochaeris radicata* L.
Spotted coralroot	*Corallorhiza maculata* Raf.
Starflower	*Trientalis latifolia* Hook.
Sticky laurel	*Ceanothus velutinus* Dougl.
Strawberry	*Fragaria* L.
Strawberry-leaf blackberry	*Rubus pedatus* J.E. Smith
Stream violet	*Viola glabella* Nutt.
Sweet cicely	*Osmorhiza* Raf.
Sword fern	*Polystichum munitum* (Kaulf.) Presl.
Thimbleberry	*Rubus parviflorus* Nutt.
Trailing raspberry	*Rubus lasiococcus* Gray and *R. nivalis* Dougl.
Trillium	*Trillium ovatum* Pursh
Twayblade	*Listera* R. Br.
Twinflower	*Linnaea borealis* L.
Twisted stalk	*Streptopus* Michx.
Valerian	*Valeriana sitchensis* Bong.
Vanilla leaf	*Achyls triphylla* (Smith) DC
Vine maple	*Acer circinatum* Pursh
Violet	*Viola* L.
Waterleaf	*Hydrophyllum*
Weeping saxifrage	*Saxifraga cernua* L.
Western coral root	*Corallorhiza mertensiana* Bong.
White-flowered rhododendron	*Rhododendron albiflorum* Hook.
White-flowered hawkweed	*Hieracium albiflorum* Hook.
Wild blackberry	*Rubus* L.
Wild cherry	*Prunus virginiana* L.
Wild ginger	*Asarum caudatum* Lindl.
Willow	*Salix* L.
Willow-herb	*Epilobium* L.
Willow weed	*Epilobium Watsonii* Barbey
Wintergreen	*Pyrola* L.
Wood nymph	*Pyrola uniflora* (L.)
Wood rose	*Rosa* L.
Wood rush	*Luzula parviflora* (Ehrh.) Desv.
Woodland beardtongue	*Nothochelone nemorosa* (Dougl.) Straw.
Yew	*Taxus brevifolia* Nutt.
Yellow violet	*Viola sempervirens* Greene

Geographic Index - Mount Rainier Area